Topic B1 — Cell Biology

Pages 1-2 — Cells

Warm up

many, plant/animal, animal/plant, single, smaller/simpler, simpler/smaller

1.1

nucleus
cytoplasm
cell membrane

[1 mark for each correct label]

1.2 Cell membrane — controls what substances go in and out of the cell ***[1 mark]***.
Cytoplasm — where most of the chemical reactions take place ***[1 mark]***.
Nucleus — controls the activities of the cell / contains genetic material ***[1 mark]***.

1.3 E.g. mitochondria ***[1 mark]*** where aerobic respiration takes place ***[1 mark]***, ribosomes ***[1 mark]*** where protein synthesis occurs ***[1 mark]***.

1.4 There is no cell wall/vacuole. / There are no chloroplasts. ***[1 mark]***

2.1 bacterium ***[1 mark]***

2.2 X – chromosome/DNA/genetic material ***[1 mark]***
Y – cell wall ***[1 mark]***
Z – plasmid ***[1 mark]***

2.3 It contains genetic material ***[1 mark]***.

2.4 10 times larger / 1 order of magnitude larger ***[1 mark]***

2.5 1 mm × 1000 = 1000 µm
1000 µm ÷ 1 µm = **1000 cells** ***[2 marks for the correct answer, otherwise 1 mark for correct working.]***

2.6 E.g. eukaryotic cells have a nucleus, prokaryotic cells do not. / DNA is found inside the nucleus of eukaryotic cells, but is not enclosed in prokaryotic cells. / Prokaryotic cells contain plasmids, eukaryotic cells do not. / Eukaryotic cells have mitochondria, prokaryotic cells do not. ***[1 mark]***

Page 3 — Microscopy

1 length of cell A in image = 24 mm
24 / 0.012 = **× 2000** ***[2 marks for the correct answer, otherwise 1 mark for correct working.]***

2.1 size of real object = size of image ÷ magnification
actual length = 10 mm ÷ 1000 = **0.01 mm** ***[2 marks for correct answer, otherwise 1 mark for correct working.]***

2.2 1 mm = 1000 µm
0.01 mm × 1000 = **10 µm** ***[1 mark]***

2.3 Electron microscopes have a higher magnification ***[1 mark]*** and a higher resolution than light microscopes ***[1 mark]***.

2.4 E.g. more cell structures can be seen under an electron microscope ***[1 mark]*** and they can be seen with greater detail ***[1 mark]***.

Page 4 — More on Microscopy

1.1 When the specimen is colourless ***[1 mark]***.

1.2 × 4 ***[1 mark]***

Remember, you should always start with the lowest-powered objective lens — this makes it easier to get your specimen into view.

1.3 They bring the sample into focus by moving the stage up and down ***[1 mark]***.

1.4 She should select the × 40 or × 10 objective lens ***[1 mark]*** and use the adjustment knobs to bring the sample back into focus ***[1 mark]***.

1.5 Any two from: e.g. she should use a pencil with a sharp point. / She should make sure her drawing takes up at least half of the space available. / She should not colour or shade her diagram. / She should ensure that the subcellular structures are drawn in proportion. / She should include a title. / She should write down the magnification that it was observed under. / She should label the important features of her drawing using straight, uncrossed lines. ***[2 marks]***

Page 5 — Cell Differentiati

Warm up

root hair cell — Long fi
area for absorption of w
xylem — Cells that are
walls form a continuous
to leaves.
phloem — Very few sub
cell walls allow dissolved sugars to move from one cell to the next.

1 differentiation ***[1 mark]***

2.1 To fertilise an egg. / To carry the male DNA to the female DNA (in the egg). ***[1 mark]***

2.2 E.g. it has a tail to enable it to swim to the egg ***[1 mark]***.
It has lots of mitochondria to give it energy ***[1 mark]***.
It has a streamlined head to aid swimming ***[1 mark]***.
The head contains enzymes to help the sperm penetrate the egg ***[1 mark]***.

Page 6 — Chromosomes and Mitosis

1.1

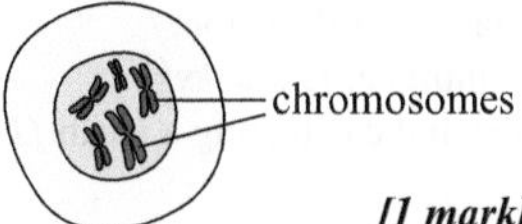

[1 mark]

1.2 DNA ***[1 mark]***

1.3 The number of subcellular structures is increasing ***[1 mark]***.
The chromosomes are doubling ***[1 mark]***.

1.4 The cytoplasm is dividing ***[1 mark]***.
The cell membrane is dividing ***[1 mark]***.

1.5 They are genetically identical ***[1 mark]***.

Pages 7-8 — Stem Cells

1.1 meristems ***[1 mark]***

1.2 E.g. plants can be produced quickly and cheaply ***[1 mark]***.
Rare species can be cloned to protect them from extinction ***[1 mark]***. Large numbers of identical crop plants with desirable features, e.g. disease resistance, can be grown for farmers ***[1 mark]***.

2.1 Stem cells can differentiate into many types of body cell ***[1 mark]***.

2.2 To increase the number of cells (available for use) ***[1 mark]***.

2.3 E.g. because body cells that are already differentiated are not capable of changing into any other types of cell ***[1 mark]***.

2.4 E.g. human embryos ***[1 mark]***

2.5 E.g. diabetes / paralysis ***[1 mark]***

2.6 E.g. the cells in the culture medium may become infected with a virus that may then be transferred to the patient ***[1 mark]***.

3.1 The production of an embryo with the same genes as a patient ***[1 mark]***.

3.2 The stem cells produced by therapeutic cloning won't be rejected by the patient's body ***[1 mark]*** because they contain the same genes as the patient ***[1 mark]***.

3.3 How to grade your answer:

Level 0: There is no relevant information. ***[No marks]***

Level 1: One or two ethical issues surrounding the use of embryonic stem cells are briefly described, but only one point of view is given. ***[1 to 2 marks]***

Level 2: A detailed discussion of issues surrounding the use of embryonic stem cells is given, including an account of both points of view. ***[3 to 4 marks]***

Here are some points your answer may include:
Some people feel that embryonic stem cells from human embryos shouldn't be used for experiments since each embryo is a potential human life.
Some people may argue that there are other sources of stem cells that scientists could use, so using embryos to create stem cells is unjustified.
Some people think that using embryonic stem cells to cure patients who already exist and who are suffering is more

important than the rights of embryos.
Some people argue that many embryonic stem cells are sourced from unwanted embryos from fertility clinics, which would probably be destroyed anyway.

Page 9 — Diffusion

Warm up

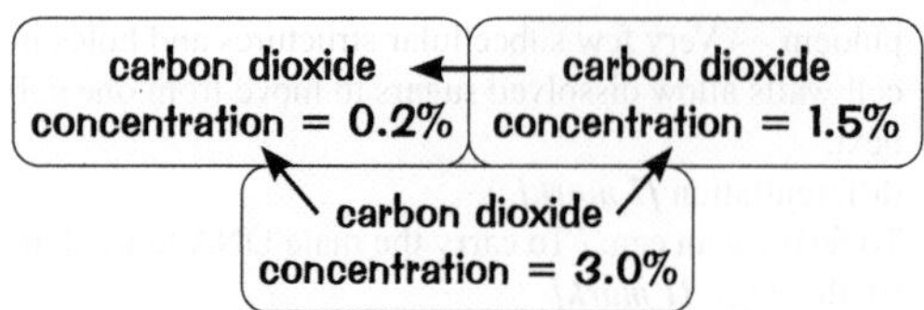

1 protein *[1 mark]*

2.1 The spreading out of particles of a gas *[1 mark]*, resulting in net movement *[1 mark]* from an area of higher concentration to an area of lower concentration *[1 mark]*.

2.2 Increasing the concentration of ammonia increases the rate of diffusion *[1 mark]*.

2.3 Any two from: e.g. the surface area of the cell. / The temperature. / The distance for diffusion. / The permeability of the membrane. *[2 marks]*

2.4 By repeating the experiment and calculating a mean *[1 mark]*.

Pages 10-11 — Osmosis

1.1 The movement of water molecules *[1 mark]* across a partially permeable membrane *[1 mark]* from a region of higher water concentration (a dilute solution) to a region of lower water concentration (a more concentrated solution) *[1 mark]*.

1.2 A plant is absorbing water from the soil *[1 mark]*.

2.1 So that all the pieces of potato have the same water concentration. / Because different potatoes will have different water concentrations. *[1 mark]*

2.2 $\frac{(6.58 - 5.73)}{5.73} \times 100$
= **14.8 %** (3 s.f.) *[2 marks for the correct answer, otherwise 1 mark for correct working.]*

2.3 E.g. 4% *[1 mark. Accept a percentage between 2% and 5%.]*

3.1 Any two from: e.g. the volume of sucrose solution the student puts in the Visking tubing. / The volume of sucrose solution the student puts in the beaker. / The temperature the beaker is kept at. / The size of the Visking tubing bag *[2 marks]*.

3.2 It will stay the same *[1 mark]*. The water concentration of the solution in the tubing is the same as the water concentration of the solution in the beaker, so there will be no net movement of water molecules *[1 mark]*.

3.3 E.g. at first, the level of the solution in the beaker will gradually increase *[1 mark]*. The water concentration of the solution in the tubing is greater than the water concentration of the solution in the beaker, so there will be a net movement of water molecules out of the tubing *[1 mark]*. Later, the level of the solution in the beaker will stop changing *[1 mark]*. The water concentration of the solutions in the tubing and the beaker will have become the same, so there will be no net movement of water molecules *[1 mark]*.

Page 12 — Active Transport

1.1 The movement of a substance from a more dilute solution to a more concentrated solution (against a concentration gradient) *[1 mark]*.

1.2 For energy/respiration *[1 mark]*.

1.3 It needs energy from respiration *[1 mark]*.

2.1 For growth *[1 mark]*.

2.2 The concentration of minerals is higher inside the plant cells than in the soil (outside the plant cells) *[1 mark]* so the minerals would move out of the plant cells by diffusion *[1 mark]*.

2.3 Active transport occurs against a concentration gradient but diffusion occurs down a concentration gradient *[1 mark]*. Active transport needs energy from respiration but diffusion doesn't *[1 mark]*.

2.4 The function of root hair cells is to take up substances from the soil *[1 mark]*. Root hair cells have elongated 'hairs' that stick out into the soil *[1 mark]*. These 'hairs' give the root a large surface area for absorbing substances *[1 mark]*.

Page 13 — Exchange Surfaces

Warm up

1 — blue whale, 2 — tiger, 3 — domestic cat, 4 — bacterium

1 A large surface area. / A thin membrane. / An efficient blood supply. / Being ventilated. *[4 marks]*

2.1 X = (3 × 3) × 6 = **54 cm²** *[1 mark]*
Y = 3 × 3 × 3 = **27 cm³** *[1 mark]*

2.2 Z = 150 ÷ 125 = **1.2** *[1 mark]*

2.3 5 × 5 × 5, because it has the smallest surface area to volume ratio / it has the most volume for the least surface area / it has the longest diffusion distance to the centre *[1 mark]*.

Page 14 — Exchanging Substances

1.1 A = carbon dioxide *[1 mark]*
B = oxygen *[1 mark]*

1.2 diffusion *[1 mark]*

1.3 short diffusion pathway — the walls of the alveoli are thin /one cell thick *[1 mark]*
large surface area — lots of alveoli *[1 mark]*

2 As the walls of the alveoli are broken down, the surface area in the lungs is reduced *[1 mark]*, so the amount of oxygen that can diffuse into the blood (from the air in the alveoli) at any one time is reduced *[1 mark]*. This means that their body cells are not getting enough oxygen for respiration during exercise, which results in lower energy levels *[1 mark]*.

3 The small intestine is covered in villi *[1 mark]* which increases the surface area for absorption *[1 mark]*.
There is a good blood supply *[1 mark]* which maintains the concentration gradient so absorption can happen quickly *[1 mark]*. The villi have a single layer of surface cells *[1 mark]* which give a short diffusion pathway *[1 mark]*.

Page 15 — More on Exchanging Substances

1.1 stomata *[1 mark]*

1.2 Carbon dioxide diffuses into the leaf *[1 mark]*.
Water vapour diffuses out of the leaf *[1 mark]*.
Oxygen diffuses out of the leaf *[1 mark]*.

1.3 They increase the surface area for carbon dioxide to diffuse into the cells *[1 mark]*.

2.1 They increase the surface area *[1 mark]*.

2.2 To (further) increase the surface area of the gills *[1 mark]*.

2.3 A good blood supply *[1 mark]*.

2.4 A fast-moving fish has more, longer gill filaments than a slow-moving fish. / A slow-moving fish has fewer, shorter gill filaments fast-moving fish. *[1 mark]*

2.5 Fast-moving fish are more active than slow-moving fish / Fast-moving fish do more respiration than slow-moving fish *[1 mark]* so they require more oxygen *[1 mark]*.

Topic B2 — Organisation

Page 16 — Cell Organisation

Warm-up

Organ system – 4, Tissue – 2, Cell – 1, Organ – 3

1.1 X = Liver *[1 mark]*
Y = Large intestine *[1 mark]*
Z = Small intestine *[1 mark]*

1.2 A group of organs working together to perform a particular function *[1 mark]*.

1.3 A group of similar cells that work together to carry out a particular function *[1 mark]*.

1.4 It breaks down and absorbs food *[1 mark]*.

1.5 A group of different tissues that work together to perform a certain function *[1 mark]*.

Page 17 — Enzymes

1.1 active site *[1 mark]*

1.2 Part X/the active site is where the substrate involved in the reaction fits *[1 mark]*.

2.1 Line 2 *[1 mark]*

2.2 Line 2 shows an enzyme with a higher optimum temperature than the enzyme shown by Line 1 *[1 mark]* and it doesn't denature until a higher temperature *[1 mark]*. This suggests that the enzyme is adapted to working at the higher temperatures of a thermal vent than the enzyme represented by Line 1 ***[1 mark]***.

2.3 The enzyme has been denatured ***[1 mark]***, which has changed the shape of its active site ***[1 mark]***. This means that the substrate will no longer fit the active site ***[1 mark]***, so the enzyme will no longer catalyse the reaction ***[1 mark]***.

Don't panic in the exam if you get a question about a context you've not met before. Just stop and think about what you know about enzymes, and it'll all become clear.

Page 18 — Investigating Enzymatic Reactions

1.1 pH 6 as this was the pH at which the iodine solution stopped turning blue-black first ***[1 mark]***, meaning the starch had been broken down the fastest ***[1 mark]***.

1.2 E.g. the amylase was denatured by the high pH, so the starch was not broken down ***[1 mark]***.

1.3 By putting the test tubes in a water bath ***[1 mark]***.

1.4 Any two from: e.g. the concentration of starch solution / the concentration of amylase / the volume of starch and amylase solution added to the iodine / the volume of iodine solution in the wells ***[2 marks]***

1.5 E.g. test the solutions more frequently (e.g. every 10 seconds) ***[1 mark]***.

Pages 19-20 — Enzymes and Digestion

Warm-up

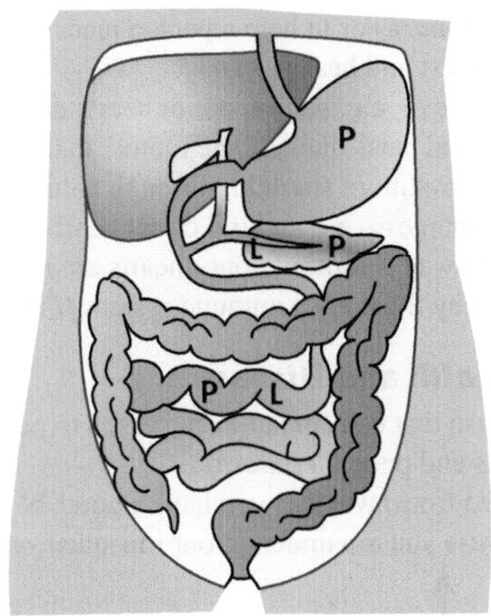

1.1 Carbohydrases ***[1 mark]***

1.2 Sugars ***[1 mark]***

2.1 They break down big molecules from food into smaller, soluble molecules that can pass easily through the walls of the digestive system ***[1 mark]***, allowing them to be absorbed into the bloodstream ***[1 mark]***.

2.2 Any two from: to make new carbohydrates. / To make new proteins. / To make new lipids. / Some glucose is used in respiration ***[2 marks]***.

3.1 Produced: liver ***[1 mark]***
Stored: gall bladder ***[1 mark]***

3.2 It neutralises the acid from the stomach in the small intestine and makes the conditions in the small intestine alkaline ***[1 mark]***. This is important because the enzymes in the small intestine work best in these conditions ***[1 mark]***. It emulsifies fat ***[1 mark]***, which increases the surface area of fat for the enzyme lipase to work on, which makes its digestion faster ***[1 mark]***.

4 How to grade your answer:

Level 0: There is no relevant information. ***[No marks]***

Level 1: There is a brief description which includes the names of one or more of the relevant enzymes or where in the body they are produced. ***[1 to 2 marks]***

Level 2: There is some description of how one or more of carbohydrates, proteins or lipids are digested, including where in the body the relevant enzymes are produced. ***[3 to 4 marks]***

Level 3: There is a clear and detailed description of how carbohydrates, proteins and lipids are digested, including reference to where in the body the relevant enzymes are produced and to the end products of the reactions. ***[5 to 6 marks]***

Here are some points your answer may include:
Carbohydrate digestion begins in the mouth, where amylase is produced by the salivary glands.
Carbohydrate digestion also occurs in the small intestine, which produces its own supply of amylase and also contains amylase produced by the pancreas.
Amylase converts the carbohydrates into sugars.
Protein is digested in the stomach, where proteases are produced.
Protein digestion also occurs in the small intestine, which produces proteases and also contains proteases produced by the pancreas.
Proteases convert protein into amino acids.
Lipids are digested in the small intestine, which produces lipases and also contains lipases produced by the pancreas.
Lipases convert lipids to fatty acids and glycerol.
The products of the digestive enzymes are absorbed into the bloodstream.

Page 21 — Food Tests

Warm-up

Biuret test — Proteins, Benedict's test — Reducing sugars, Sudan III test — Lipids, Iodine test — Starch

1 How to grade your answer:

Level 0: There is no relevant information. ***[No marks]***

Level 1: There is a brief description of how to carry out the investigation. ***[1 to 2 marks]***

Level 2: There is some description of how to carry out the investigation but some details are missing. ***[3 to 4 marks]***

Level 3: There is a clear and detailed description of how to carry out the investigation. ***[5 to 6 marks]***

Here are some points your answer may include:
Grind up a sample of the egg white using a pestle and mortar.
Put the sample into a beaker and add some distilled water.
Stir well with a glass rod to allow some of the food to dissolve in the water.
Filter the mixture through a funnel lined with filter paper.
Transfer 2 cm^3 of the filtered solution into a clean test tube.
Add 2 cm^3 of Biuret solution and gently shake the test tube.
If the food sample contains protein, the solution will change from blue to pink or purple.
If no protein is present, the solution will stay bright blue.

2.1 He should add some Benedict's solution to each test tube using a pipette ***[1 mark]***. He should then place the test tubes in a water bath set at 75 °C and leave them for 5 minutes ***[1 mark]***. He should look out for a colour change and note which of a range of colours the solutions become ***[1 mark]***.

Glucose is a reducing sugar so the Benedict's test can be used to determine the relative concentrations of glucose in the test tubes.

2.2

	Tube 1	Tube 2	Tube 3	Tube 4
substance observed	yellow precipitate	blue solution	red precipitate	green precipitate
glucose concentration (M)	**0.1**	**0**	**1**	**0.02**

[1 mark]

The higher the concentration of glucose in the solution, the further the colour change goes along the following scale: blue — green — yellow — brick red. If no precipitate forms then there are no reducing sugars in the solution.

Page 22 — The Lungs

Warm-up

bronchi, alveoli, oxygenates, carbon dioxide

1.1 A = trachea ***[1 mark]***
B = bronchus ***[1 mark]***
C = alveolus/alveoli ***[1 mark]***

1.2 capillary ***[1 mark]***

1.3 The capillary carries blood that is returning from the rest of the body and contains a higher concentration of carbon dioxide than in the lungs ***[1 mark]***. The carbon dioxide diffuses into the alveoli, where there is a lower concentration, to be breathed out ***[1 mark]***. The capillary also picks up oxygen from the alveoli, which contain a higher concentration of oxygen than in the blood ***[1 mark]***. Oxygen diffuses from the alveoli into the blood, where there is a lower concentration, to be carried to the body cells ***[1 mark]***.

Page 23 — Circulatory System — The Heart

1.1 X = aorta
Y = pulmonary vein
Z = (right) ventricle

1.2

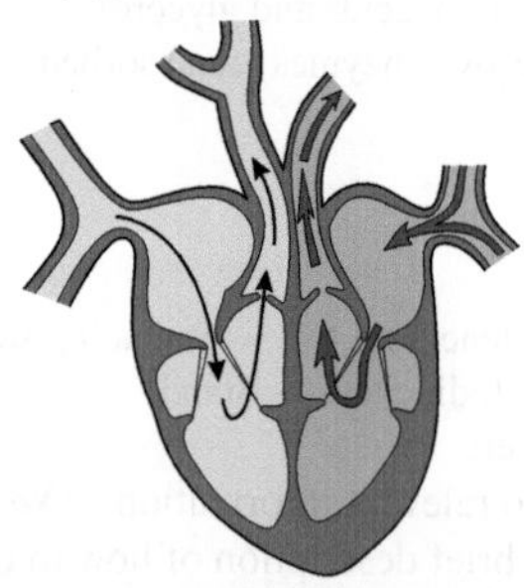

[1 mark for arrow(s) showing blood flow from the vena cava, through the right atrium and ventricle, then up through the pulmonary artery.]

1.3 Because it consists of two circuits joined together ***[1 mark]***. The first one pumps deoxygenated blood to the lungs to take in oxygen and returns oxygenated blood to the heart ***[1 mark]***. The second one pumps oxygenated blood around all the other organs of the body and returns deoxygenated blood to the heart ***[1 mark]***.

2.1 The heartbeat is controlled by a group of cells in the right atrium wall ***[1 mark]*** that act as a pacemaker ***[1 mark]***.

2.2 An artificial pacemaker could be fitted ***[1 mark]***. This produces an electric current to keep the heart beating regularly ***[1 mark]***.

Pages 24-25 — Circulatory System — Blood Vessels

1.1 A ***[1 mark]***

1.2 The walls of arteries contain thick layers of muscle to make them strong ***[1 mark]*** and elastic fibres to allow them to stretch and spring back ***[1 mark]***.

1.3 veins ***[1 mark]***

1.4 To prevent the blood flowing backwards / to keep the blood flowing in the right direction ***[1 mark]***.

1.5 Capillaries carry blood close to cells to exchange substances with them ***[1 mark]***. Having thin walls increases the rate at which substances can diffuse across them by decreasing the distance over which diffusion occurs ***[1 mark]***.

2.1 E.g. the graph shows that as an increasing amount of mass was added and then removed from the ring of artery, the percentage change in the ring's length remained at 0 ***[1 mark]***, so the ring returned to its original length each time the mass was removed ***[1 mark]***. As the amount of mass added and then removed from the ring of vein increased, the percentage change in the ring's length increased ***[1 mark]***, so the ring did not return to its original length once the mass was removed and the greater the mass, the further it was from its original length ***[1 mark]***.

2.2 Any sensible precaution, e.g. wear safety goggles / wear gloves / disinfect the workstation after the experiment / wash hands after the experiment ***[1 mark]***.

Page 26 — Circulatory System — Blood

1.1 Because white blood cells defend against infection ***[1 mark]***.

1.2 Some white blood cells can change shape to engulf microorganisms in a process called phagocytosis ***[1 mark]***. Others produce antibodies to fight microorganisms ***[1 mark]*** or antitoxins to neutralise any toxins produced by the microorganisms ***[1 mark]***.

1.3 They have a biconcave disc shape to give a large surface area for absorbing oxygen ***[1 mark]***. They don't have a nucleus, which allows more room to carry oxygen ***[1 mark]***. They contain haemoglobin, which binds to oxygen and transports it to cells in the body tissues ***[1 mark]***.

1.4 plasma ***[1 mark]***

1.5 Platelets are small fragments of cells with no nucleus ***[1 mark]***. They help the blood to clot at a wound ***[1 mark]***.

Pages 27-28 — Cardiovascular Disease

Warm-up

blood vessels, coronary heart disease, coronary arteries, fatty material

1.1 Because it restricts the blood flow to the heart muscle ***[1 mark]***, leading to a lack of oxygen reaching it ***[1 mark]***.

1.2 The doctor might recommend a stent ***[1 mark]***. Stents are tubes that are inserted inside arteries to keep them open to make sure that blood can pass through to the heart muscle ***[1 mark]***.

2.1 They reduce the amount of 'bad' cholesterol present in the bloodstream ***[1 mark]***. This slows down the rate of fatty deposits forming in the coronary arteries ***[1 mark]***.

2.2 E.g. he is worried about side effects the statins might cause ***[1 mark]***.

3.1 It would allow the blood to flow in both directions in part of the heart ***[1 mark]***, meaning that blood doesn't circulate around the body as effectively as normal ***[1 mark]***.

3.2 It might not open fully ***[1 mark]***.

3.3 A valve taken from a human or another mammal ***[1 mark]***.

3.4 A man-made/artificial valve ***[1 mark]***.

3.5 To keep a patient alive while waiting for a donor heart to be found ***[1 mark]*** or to help a person recover by allowing their heart to rest and heal ***[1 mark]***.

3.6 Advantage — e.g. natural donor hearts don't have any mechanical parts like electric motors that could wear out. / Blood flows more smoothly through natural hearts ***[1 mark]***.
Disadvantage — e.g. natural donor hearts aren't always available straight away. / Natural donor hearts are more likely to be rejected by the body's immune system ***[1 mark]***.

Page 29 — Health and Disease

1.1 A disease that can spread from person to person or between animals and people ***[1 mark]***.

1.2 Any two from: whether you have a good, balanced diet. / The stress you are under. / Your life situation ***[2 marks]***.

2.1

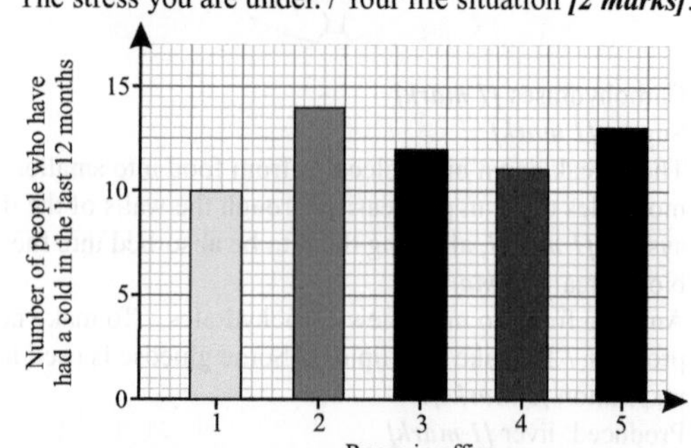

[1 mark for each correctly drawn bar for rooms 3 and 5.]

Room 1	Room 2	Room 3	Room 4	Room 5	Total
10	**14**	12	11	**13**	60

[1 mark for each number filled in correctly.]

You're given the total number of people who have had colds in the table (60). So to work out the figure for Room 5, you'd take the total for Rooms 1–4 away from 60.

2.2 It would increase the chance of the person getting a communicable disease ***[1 mark]*** because their body is less likely to be able to defend itself against the pathogen that causes the disease ***[1 mark]***.

Pages 30-31 — Risk Factors for Non-Communicable Diseases

1.1 Something that is linked to an increase in the likelihood that a person will develop a certain disease during their lifetime ***[1 mark]***.

1.2 Aspects of a person's lifestyle ***[1 mark]***. Substances in the body ***[1 mark]***.

1.3 E.g. type 2 diabetes ***[1 mark]***

2.1 Any two from: e.g. a high fat diet / a lack of exercise / smoking ***[2 marks]***

2.2 Any two from: e.g. the cost of researching and treating non-communicable diseases is huge. / Families may have to move or adapt their home to help a family member with a non-communicable disease, which can be costly. / If someone has to give up work/dies because of a non-communicable disease, family income will reduce. / A reduction in the people able to work may affect a country's economy ***[2 marks]***.

3.1 The number of people with diabetes increased between 2012 and 2018 ***[1 mark]***.

3.2 How to grade your answer:

Level 0: There is no relevant information. ***[No marks]***

Level 1: One or two comments about the student's statements are made but only points in support of or against the student's statement are given. ***[1 to 2 marks]***

Level 2: A detailed discussion of the student's statement is given, including points both in support and against. ***[3 to 4 marks]***

Here are some points your answer may include:

<u>In support of the student's statement:</u>

Both graphs show an overall positive correlation. / Both the rate of obesity and the rate of diabetes increase overall between 2012 and 2018.

It is generally accepted that obesity is a risk factor for Type 2 diabetes.

<u>Against the student's statement:</u>

A correlation between the number of people with diabetes and the prevalence of obesity doesn't show that diabetes is caused by obesity — there may be another factor that affects both.

Figure 1 shows that the percentage of people with obesity fell between 2015 and 2016, while the number of people with diabetes increased in the same year, which contradicts the student's statement.

The student is only comparing data for seven years — it may be that the trend is not present over a longer period of time.

Page 32 — Cancer

Warm-up

Malignant Tumours — Are cancerous

Malignant Tumours — Can invade neighbouring tissues

Benign Tumours — Are not cancerous

1.1 Uncontrolled cell division ***[1 mark]***

1.2 genetic risk factors ***[1 mark]***

2.1 malignant ***[1 mark]***

2.2 Cells break off a tumour and spread to other parts of the body by travelling in the bloodstream ***[1 mark]***. The malignant cells then invade healthy tissues elsewhere in the body and form secondary tumours ***[1 mark]***.

Page 33 — Plant Cell Organisation

1.1 An organ system ***[1 mark]***

1.2 Water ***[1 mark]***, mineral ions ***[1 mark]***

2.1 Growing tips of roots ***[1 mark]***
Growing tips of shoots ***[1 mark]***

2.2 It can differentiate into lots of different types of plant cells ***[1 mark]***.

3.1 A: palisade mesophyll tissue ***[1 mark]***
B: spongy mesophyll tissue ***[1 mark]***

3.2 It contains lots of chloroplasts, which are the structures where photosynthesis takes place ***[1 mark]*** and is located near the top of the leaf so that the chloroplasts can get the most light ***[1 mark]***.

3.3 They increase the rate of diffusion of gases ***[1 mark]***.

Page 34 — Transpiration and Translocation

Warm-up

transpiration, evaporation, leaves, translocation, sugars, phloem

1 How to grade your answer:

Level 0: There is no relevant information. ***[No marks]***

Level 1: There is a brief description of either the structure or the function of one or both of the plant tissues. ***[1 to 2 marks]***

Level 2: There is some description of both the structure and the function of both plant tissues. ***[3 to 4 marks]***

Level 3: There is detailed description of both the structure and the function of both plant tissues. ***[5 to 6 marks]***

Here are some points your answer may include:

Xylem is made of dead cells joined together end to end.

The walls are strengthened with lignin.

The dead cells have no end walls between them, so there is a hole down the middle of the tissue.

Water and mineral ions travel through the xylem tubes from the roots to the stem and leaves.

This is called the transpiration stream.

Phloem is made of columns of elongated living cells.

The cells have small pores in the end walls to allow cell sap to flow through.

This means that dissolved sugars made in the leaves can travel to the rest of the plant.

Phloem can transport dissolved sugars in both directions in the tissue.

Transport of dissolved sugars in phloem is called translocation.

Page 35-36 — Transpiration and Stomata

1.1 X = stomata ***[1 mark]***
Y = guard cells ***[1 mark]***

1.2 They are responsible for opening and closing the stomata ***[1 mark]*** in order to control gas exchange and water loss from a leaf ***[1 mark]***.

2.1 Mean width of stomata in leaf A =
(25.2 + 20.1 + 18.7 + 17.9 + 19.1 + 19.3 + 22.0 + 23.1 + 21.8 + 20.3) ÷ 10 = **20.8 μm** ***[1 mark]***

Mean width of stomata in leaf B =
(14.7 + 12.8 + 14.1 + 13.2 + 12.9 + 11.9 + 12.1 + 13.4 + 10.9 + 11.7) ÷ 10 = **12.8 μm** ***[1 mark]***

2.2 Leaf B ***[1 mark]***

2.3 Because stomata begin to close when it gets darker / Less carbon dioxide is needed for photosynthesis at lower light intensities ***[1 mark]*** and so the leaf with the lower mean will have had the measurements taken in a lower light intensity ***[1 mark]***.

3.1

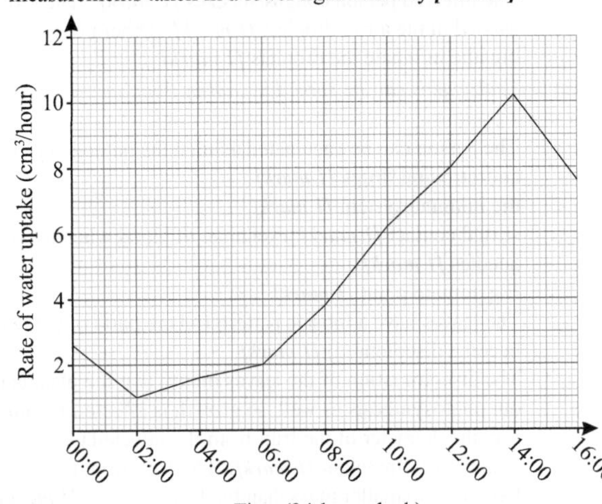

[1 mark for using a sensible scale for the y-axis, 1 mark for labelling the y-axis, 1 mark for accurately plotting the points, 1 mark for connecting the points with straight lines through the centre of each point.]

It might sound a bit obvious, but make sure you always use a sharp pencil to draw graphs like this. Your graph might turn out inaccurate if your pencil is blunt, which could lose you marks.

3.2 5.0 cm^3/hour ***[1 mark]***

3.3 5.1 cm^3/hour ***[1 mark]***

3.4 Any two from: e.g. light intensity increased. / Temperature increased. / Air flow around the leaf improved. / Humidity decreased ***[2 marks]***.

Topic B3 — Infection and Response

Page 37 — Communicable Disease

1.1 Both bacteria and viruses can reproduce quickly in the body ***[1 mark]***.

1.2 It can cause the cells to burst ***[1 mark]***.

2 How to grade your answer:

Level 0: There is no relevant information. ***[No marks]***

Level 1: There is a brief description of either how the housefly picks up pathogens or how it spreads them to humans. ***[1 to 2 marks]***

Level 2: There is some description of how the housefly picks up pathogens and how it spreads them to humans. ***[3 to 4 marks]***

Level 3: There is a detailed description of how the housefly picks up pathogens and how it spreads them to humans. ***[5 to 6 marks]***

Here are some points your answer may include:

Picking up pathogens:

The housefly uses its wings to fly to a dirty place, e.g. animal faeces, dustbin, rubbish dump, etc.
Pathogens stick to the fly's body.
Pathogens stick to the hairs on the fly's legs.
Pathogens are picked up on the fly's wings.
Pathogens are eaten by the fly.

Transfer to humans:

The fly uses its wings to travel to a human food source.
The fly secretes saliva on a human food source along with pathogens that the fly ate.
The housefly transfers pathogens onto a human food source from its body/leg hairs/wings.
The housefly deposits faeces onto a human food source.
Humans then eat the contaminated food source and take in the pathogens.

Pages 38-39 — Viral, Fungal and Protist Diseases

Warm-up

protist, vectors, fever, breeding

1.1 virus ***[1 mark]***

1.2 The infected person coughs/sneezes ***[1 mark]***. The virus is carried in the air in droplets ***[1 mark]***. Other people on the train breathe in/inhale the droplets ***[1 mark]***.

Remember, pathogens can be spread by water, through the air, by vectors, or by direct contact.

1.3 The person can be vaccinated against the pathogen ***[1 mark]***.

2.1 antiretroviral drugs ***[1 mark]***

2.2 the immune system ***[1 mark]***

2.3 sexual contact ***[1 mark]***, exchange of blood when people share needles ***[1 mark]***

3.1 E.g. tomato plant ***[1 mark]***

3.2 The leaves have a mosaic pattern (where parts of the leaves become discoloured) ***[1 mark]***.

3.3 The discolouration of the leaves means that the plant can't carry out photosynthesis as well, so growth is affected ***[1 mark]***.

3.4 E.g. the diameter of the fruit from the infected plant is smaller than the healthy plant ***[1 mark]***. The fruit from the infected plant has a lower/smaller mass than the healthy plant ***[1 mark]***.

4.1 Purple or black spots develop on the leaves ***[1 mark]***. These leaves can then turn yellow ***[1 mark]*** and drop off ***[1 mark]***.

4.2 Because the disease can spread to other plants in water or by the wind ***[1 mark]***.

4.3 If any leaves are left, the fungus could spread to other living rose plants ***[1 mark]***.

By destroying the fungus, there won't be any left to spread to other plants.

Page 40 — Bacterial Diseases and Preventing Disease

1.1 Any two from: e.g. fever / stomach cramps / vomiting / diarrhoea ***[2 marks]***.

1.2 toxins ***[1 mark]***

1.3 The vaccination prevents the spread of the disease in poultry ***[1 mark]***. This means that the poultry that humans eat won't be contaminated with the *Salmonella* bacteria ***[1 mark]***.

1.4 E.g. by washing hands thoroughly after using the toilet. / By avoiding preparing food. / By the infected person being isolated from other individuals ***[1 mark]***.

There's more than one right answer here — just think of any sensible way of preventing the bacteria from being transferred from person to person.

2.1 Through sexual contact ***[1 mark]***.

2.2 E.g. pain when urinating ***[1 mark]***. A thick yellow or green discharge from the vagina ***[1 mark]***.

2.3 penicillin ***[1 mark]***

2.4 condoms ***[1 mark]***

Page 41 — Fighting Disease

1.1 It acts as a barrier to stop pathogens getting inside the body ***[1 mark]***. It secretes antimicrobial substances, which kill pathogens ***[1 mark]***.

1.2 It has hairs and mucus, which trap particles that could contain pathogens ***[1 mark]***.

2 How to grade your answer:

Level 0: There is no relevant information. ***[No marks]***

Level 1: There is a brief description of either the body's defences or the role of the immune system. ***[1 to 2 marks]***

Level 2: There is at least one correct description of the body's defences and at least one correct description of the role of the immune system. ***[3 to 4 marks]***

Level 3: There is more than one correct description of the body's defences and more than one correct description of the role of the immune system. ***[5 to 6 marks]***

Here are some points your answer may include:

The body's defences:

The trachea and bronchi secrete mucus to trap pathogens that have entered the body.
The trachea and bronchi are lined with cilia.
Cilia are hair-like structures which waft mucus up to the back of the throat where it can be swallowed.
The stomach produces hydrochloric acid, which kills pathogens that have been swallowed.

The role of the immune system:

The immune system contains white blood cells, which travel round the body in the blood.
White blood cells can engulf pathogens and digest them — this is called phagocytosis.
White blood cells can produce antibodies that can kill pathogens.
White blood cells can produce antitoxins that counteract toxins produced by invading bacteria.

You wouldn't get marks for talking about the skin or about the hairs in the nose — they're there to stop pathogens getting inside your body in the first place. This question is asking you to describe that defences that the body has for pathogens that have managed to make it inside your body.

Page 42 — Fighting Disease — Vaccination

1.1 small amounts of dead/inactive pathogens ***[1 mark]***

1.2 White blood cells are stimulated to produce antibodies ***[1 mark]***.

2.1 Because the body would be able to rapidly mass-produce antibodies to kill off the mumps pathogens ***[1 mark]***.

2.2 The large proportion of the population who have been vaccinated against the pathogen won't catch the disease ***[1 mark]***. This means that the people who aren't vaccinated are unlikely to catch the disease because there are fewer people able to pass it on ***[1 mark]***.

3.1 It would prevent the traveller from catching cholera whilst they are visiting the country ***[1 mark]*** and then bringing it back to their own country ***[1 mark]***.

3.2 It prevents anyone from bringing certain diseases into the country ***[1 mark]***.

Page 43 — Fighting Disease — Drugs

1.1 Viruses reproduce using your body cells ***[1 mark]***, which makes it very difficult to develop drugs that destroy just the virus without killing the body's cells ***[1 mark]***.

1.2 E.g. painkiller / cold remedy ***[1 mark]***

1.3 Because the drug is unable to kill pathogens ***[1 mark]***.

2.1 Bacteria that can't be killed by an antibiotic ***[1 mark]***.

2.2 The number of antibiotic-resistant infections increased between

2013 and 2015 ***[1 mark]***.

2.3 153 – 84 = 69
(69 ÷ 84) × 100 = 82.14 = **82%** ***[2 marks for correct answer, otherwise 1 mark for correct working.]***

Page 44 — Developing Drugs

1.1 E.g. toxicity, efficacy and dosage ***[3 marks]***

1.2 cells, tissues and live animals ***[1 mark]***

It'd be no use testing on dead animals, as their cells and tissues won't respond in the same way as living tissues. You also wouldn't want to test on humans or patients at this stage, just in case the drug proves to be dangerous.

2.1 In case the drug has any harmful effects ***[1 mark]***.

2.2 In double blind trials, patients would be randomly split into two groups ***[1 mark]***. One group would be given a placebo and the other group would be given the drug ***[1 mark]***. Neither the patients or the doctors would know who was in which group until after the results had been gathered ***[1 mark]***.

2.3 It allows for the placebo effect. / It prevents the patient expecting the treatment to work and therefore feeling better, even though the treatment isn't doing anything. / It prevents the doctors who are analysing the results from being subconsciously influenced by their knowledge. ***[1 mark]***

2.4 E.g. it helps to check that the work is valid. / It helps to prevent false claims ***[1 mark]***.

2.5 E.g. to prevent them showing bias ***[1 mark]*** in their analysis of the results, and giving support to the results when in fact they weren't valid ***[1 mark]***.

Topic B4 — Bioenergetics

Page 45 — Photosynthesis and Limiting Factors

1.1 the Sun / the environment ***[1 mark]***

1.2 **carbon dioxide** ***[1 mark]*** + water → glucose + **oxygen** ***[1 mark]***

1.3 cellulose ***[1 mark]***

1.4 Any two from: e.g. for respiration. / For making amino acids (which are used to make proteins) by combining the glucose with nitrate ions. / It is converted to lipids (fats and oils) for storage. / It is turned into starch for storage ***[2 marks]***.

2.1 An endothermic reaction is where energy is transferred from the environment during the process ***[1 mark]***.

2.2 nitrate concentration ***[1 mark]***

2.3 The rate of photosynthesis would decrease ***[1 mark]*** because the chloroplasts wouldn't be able to absorb as much light ***[1 mark]***.

Pages 46-48 — The Rate of Photosynthesis

Warm-up

low, slowly, high, damaged

1.1 Any two from: e.g. adding a heater — to increase the temperature, which will increase the rate of photosynthesis. / Supplying artificial light — to increase the light intensity, which will increase the rate of photosynthesis. / Adding a paraffin heater — to increase the carbon dioxide concentration, which will increase the rate of photosynthesis. ***[1 mark for each correct improvement and 1 mark for each correct explanation, up to 4 marks.]***

1.2 Because the farmer will get a better yield ***[1 mark]***, which means they will also make more money/profit ***[1 mark]***.

2.1 At first, as the carbon dioxide concentration increases, the rate of photosynthesis increases as well ***[1 mark]***. Then, at 0.10 arbitrary units of carbon dioxide, the graph flattens out — as the carbon dioxide concentration increases, the rate of photosynthesis no longer increases ***[1 mark]***.

2.2 E.g. temperature ***[1 mark]***, light intensity ***[1 mark]***

2.3

Rate of photosynthesis (arbitrary units)

Light intensity (arbitrary units)

[1 mark for correctly labelled axes, 1 mark for correctly sketched line.]

3.1 It will increase ***[1 mark]***.

3.2 distance = 20 cm, so $20^2 = 400$ ***[1 mark]***
1 ÷ 400 = **0.0025 arbitrary units** ***[1 mark]***

3.3 How to grade your answer:

Level 0: There is no relevant information. ***[No marks]***

Level 1: There is a brief description of a method used to investigate the effect of temperature on the rate of photosynthesis, with no control variables mentioned. ***[1 to 2 marks]***

Level 2: There is some description of a method used to investigate the effect of temperature on the rate of photosynthesis, including an example of a variable to control. ***[3 to 4 marks]***

Level 3: There is detailed description of a method used to investigate the effect of temperature on the rate of photosynthesis, including more than one example of variables to control. ***[5 to 6 marks]***

Here are some points your answer may include:
A test tube is clamped in place in a water bath at a particular temperature, e.g. 10 °C.
Once the water in the test tube has reached the correct temperature, the pondweed is added to the test tube and the test tube is sealed.
A capillary tube and syringe are attached to the test tube.
The pondweed is left to photosynthesise for a set amount of time.
At the end of the experiment, the syringe is used to draw the gas bubble in the capillary tube up alongside a ruler and the length of the gas bubble that has formed is measured. This is proportional to the volume of oxygen produced.
The experiment is repeated twice at this starting temperature.
Then the whole experiment is repeated at different temperatures, e.g. 15 °C, 20 °C, 25 °C.
The variables that should be controlled in this experiment include light intensity and the concentration of carbon dioxide.

Pages 49-50 — Respiration and Metabolism

1.1 exothermic (reaction) ***[1 mark]***

1.2 E.g. to build up larger molecules from smaller ones ***[1 mark]***.
To allow the gull's muscles to contract ***[1 mark]***. To keep the gull's body temperature steady in cooler surroundings ***[1 mark]***.

2.1 Plants, e.g: cellulose / starch / proteins ***[1 mark]***
Animals, e.g: glycogen / proteins ***[1 mark]***

2.2 A lipid is made from one molecule of glycerol ***[1 mark]*** and three fatty acids ***[1 mark]***.

2.3 Glucose is combined with nitrate ions ***[1 mark]*** to make amino acids, which are then made into proteins ***[1 mark]***.

2.4 urea ***[1 mark]***

3.1 Any two from, e.g. the mass of the peas or glass beads in the flask / the size of the flask / the type of peas / the temperature outside of the flasks / the temperature of the peas at the start of the experiment ***[2 marks]***.

3.2 E.g. she could repeat her experiment and calculate a mean temperature increase for each flask ***[1 mark]***.

3.3 The boiled peas will not germinate, so flask 2 is included to show that the increase in temperature in flask 1 is due to the peas germinating ***[1 mark]***. Flask 3 is included to show that the temperature change is due to the presence of the peas and no other factor ***[1 mark]***.

The temperature in flask 3 should remain constant — if it changed, this would suggest there was an error in the experiment.

3.4 E.g. she could include another flask that contained disinfected boiled peas. / She could disinfect the peas (and the glass beads) with an antiseptic before starting the experiment ***[1 mark]***.

If there was no temperature change in a flask containing disinfected boiled peas, the student could conclude that the temperature increase in the flask of boiled peas in her first experiment was due to the presence of microorganisms.

Pages 51-52 — Aerobic and Anaerobic Respiration

Warm-up

Aerobic respiration — Respiration using oxygen.
Anaerobic respiration — Respiration without oxygen.
Fermentation — Respiration without oxygen.

1.1 E.g. the snail must have enough oxygen for two hours / the snail must not dry out *[1 mark]*.
1.2 The percentage of carbon dioxide in the air has increased over the two hours because the snail gives out carbon dioxide as it respires *[1 mark]*.
1.3 The percentage of carbon dioxide in the air has stayed the same over the two hours because the glass beads were not respiring *[1 mark]*.
1.4 It will have decreased *[1 mark]* because the snail will have used up oxygen as it respired *[1 mark]*.
1.5 To show that it's the snail producing carbon dioxide (and not just the presence of something in the beaker) *[1 mark]*.
2.1 glucose *[1 mark]*
2.2 Ethanol — to make alcoholic drinks *[1 mark]*.
Carbon dioxide — to make bread rise *[1 mark]*.
3 Aerobic respiration in muscle cells uses oxygen, whereas anaerobic respiration doesn't *[1 mark]*. Aerobic respiration in muscle cells forms carbon dioxide and water, whereas anaerobic respiration forms lactic acid *[1 mark]*. Aerobic respiration in muscles cells transfers a lot of energy, whereas anaerobic respiration in muscle cells transfers a small amount of energy *[1 mark]*.

Pages 53-54 — Exercise

Warm-up
muscles, oxygen debt, oxygen, lactic acid
1.1 (12 + 11 + 12) ÷ 3 = 11.6... = **12** breaths per minute *[1 mark]*
1.2 During exercise the breathing rate increased *[1 mark]* to get more oxygen into the blood *[1 mark]*, which was needed for increased respiration in the muscles *[1 mark]*.
1.3 The breathing rate remained high one minute after exercise *[1 mark]* because there were still high levels of lactic acid and carbon dioxide in the blood *[1 mark]*. The high breathing rate helps remove these from the body *[1 mark]*. The breathing rate had returned to normal by five minutes after exercise *[1 mark]* because the oxygen debt had been paid off *[1 mark]*.
1.4 breath volume *[1 mark]*, heart rate *[1 mark]*
2.1 80 – 20 = 60
(60 ÷ 20) × 100 = **300%** *[2 marks for correct answer, otherwise 1 mark for correct working.]*
2.2 The muscles started to respire anaerobically *[1 mark]*, which formed lactic acid *[1 mark]* as a result of the incomplete oxidation of glucose *[1 mark]*.
2.3 They become fatigued *[1 mark]* and stop contracting efficiently *[1 mark]*.
2.4 Blood transports the lactic acid to the liver *[1 mark]*, where it is converted back to glucose *[1 mark]*.

Topic B5 — Homeostasis and Response

Page 55 — Homeostasis

1.1 The regulation of the conditions inside the body/cells to maintain a stable internal environment *[1 mark]* in response to changes in internal and external conditions *[1 mark]*.
1.2 They maintain the right conditions for cells to function properly. / They maintain the right conditions for enzyme action. *[1 mark]*
1.3 receptor *[1 mark]*
1.4 The receptors detect that the blood pressure is too high and send a signal to the coordination centre *[1 mark]*. The coordination centre processes the information and organises a response / stimulates an effector *[1 mark]*. The effector produces a response to decrease the blood pressure (back to its optimum level) *[1 mark]*.
You don't need to know all about the regulation of blood pressure to answer this question — you just need to know the sequence of events in a negative feedback response, from receptors to effectors.
2.1 15 minutes *[1 mark]*
2.2 30 – 20 = 10 min, 35.0 – 34.5 = 0.5 °C
0.5 ÷ 10 = **0.05 °C/min** *[2 marks for correct answer, otherwise 1 mark for correct working.]*

Pages 56-57 — The Nervous System

1.1 X — brain *[1 mark]*
Y— spinal cord *[1 mark]*
1.2 central nervous system/CNS *[1 mark]*
1.3 It receives information from receptors and coordinates a response (which is carried out by effectors) *[1 mark]*.
2.1 It allows organisms to react to their surroundings *[1 mark]* and coordinate their behaviour *[1 mark]*.
2.2 Spinal cord — coordinator *[1 mark]*
Bright light — stimulus *[1 mark]*
Blinking — response *[1 mark]*
2.3 Sensory neurones *[1 mark]* and motor neurones *[1 mark]*.
2.4 Muscles — contract *[1 mark]*
Glands — secrete hormones *[1 mark]*
3.1 E.g. it will reduce the effect of random errors on their results *[1 mark]*.
3.2 uncertainty = range ÷ 2 = (25 – 15) ÷ 2 = 10 ÷ 2
= **± 5 mm** *[2 marks for correct answer, otherwise 1 mark for correct working.]*
3.3 E.g. move the toothpicks together at smaller intervals (e.g. 1 mm) around the point where the person can only feel one toothpick *[1 mark]*.
3.4 Repeat the experiment on the forearm more times to see if it still doesn't fit in with the rest of the results *[1 mark]*
3.5 The students have only tested three parts of the body / they haven't tested all parts of the body *[1 mark]*, so they can only conclude that the palm is the most sensitive out of the parts tested *[1 mark]*.

Page 58 — Synapses and Reflexes

Warm-up
Dropping a hot plate. The pupil widening in dim light.
1 Reflex reactions are rapid and automatic. *[1 mark]*
2.1 X — sensory neurone *[1 mark]*
Y — relay neurone *[1 mark]*
Z — motor neurone *[1 mark]*
2.2 stimulus — flame/fire *[1 mark]*
coordinator — spinal cord / relay neurone *[1 mark]*
effector — muscle *[1 mark]*
2.3 synapse *[1 mark]*
2.4 Chemicals diffuse across the gap and transfer the nerve signal *[1 mark]*.

Page 59 — Investigating Reaction Time

1.1 Student 2 = (0.16 + 0.13 + 0.15) ÷ 3 = 0.1466...
= **0.15 s** *[1 mark]*
Student 3 = (0.20 + 0.22 + 0.19) ÷ 3 = 0.2033...
= **0.20 s** *[1 mark]*
1.2 Student 1, Test 3 (0.43 s) *[1 mark]*
1.3 The students' reaction times without caffeine would act as a control for each student *[1 mark]*. The results from each student's tests could then be compared to the control to see if caffeine actually had an effect on reaction time *[1 mark]*.
1.4 E.g. the reaction times of student 1, 2 and 3 will be affected to different extents by caffeine due to natural variation between them *[1 mark]*, so the investigation isn't a fair test *[1 mark]*. / Two variables (the caffeinated drink and the student) are being changed *[1 mark]*, so the investigation isn't a fair test *[1 mark]*.
1.5 Any three from: e.g. the hand that the student used to catch the ruler. / The height from which the ruler was dropped. / The ruler used. / The person dropping the ruler. / The way that the student was positioned to catch the ruler. / The time between the consumption of caffeine and the test.
[3 marks — 1 mark for each correct answer.]
You wouldn't get a mark for saying that the amount of caffeine given to each student should be the same each time — this was said in the question.

Page 60 — The Endocrine System

1.1 Glands secrete hormones directly into the blood. *[1 mark]*
1.2 Hormones are chemical molecules. *[1 mark]*
1.3 E.g. the effects of the endocrine system are slower *[1 mark]*. The effects of the endocrine system are longer lasting *[1 mark]*.
2.1 A — pituitary gland *[1 mark]*
B — thyroid *[1 mark]*
C — adrenal gland *[1 mark]*
D — pancreas *[1 mark]*
E — ovary *[1 mark]*

2.2 pituitary gland *[1 mark]*
2.3 They act on other glands *[1 mark]* to direct them to release other hormones that bring about change *[1 mark]*.

Page 61-62 — Controlling Blood Glucose

1.1 pancreas *[1 mark]*
1.2 insulin *[1 mark]*
1.3 It moves into liver and muscle cells *[1 mark]* and is converted to glycogen for storage *[1 mark]*.
2.1 The pancreas produces little or no insulin *[1 mark]*.
2.2 Uncontrolled high blood glucose level *[1 mark]*.
2.3 E.g. the person's diet. / How active the person is. *[1 mark]*
2.4 The body cells no longer respond to the insulin produced by the pancreas *[1 mark]*.
2.5 Eat a carbohydrate-controlled diet *[1 mark]* and get regular exercise *[1 mark]*.
2.6 being overweight / obesity *[1 mark]*
3.1 The blood glucose concentration starts increasing as glucose from the drink is absorbed into the blood *[1 mark]*.
The pancreas detects a high blood glucose concentration and secretes insulin *[1 mark]*. Insulin causes the blood glucose concentration to fall back down *[1 mark]*.
3.2 glucagon *[1 mark]*
3.3 It increases the concentration of glucose in the blood *[1 mark]*.
3.4 Glucagon causes glycogen to be converted into glucose and be released into the blood *[1 mark]*.
3.5 E.g. after drinking the glucose drink, the blood glucose concentration would carry on increasing / stay high / not start to fall / fall more slowly *[1 mark]*.

Page 63 — Puberty and the Menstrual Cycle

1.1 oestrogen *[1 mark]*
1.2 ovulation *[1 mark]*
1.3 Every 28 days *[1 mark]*
1.4 luteinising hormone *[1 mark]*
1.5 testosterone *[1 mark]*
1.6 testes *[1 mark]*
2.1 oestrogen *[1 mark]*, progesterone *[1 mark]*
2.2 pituitary gland *[1 mark]*
2.3 It causes an egg to mature in one of the ovaries *[1 mark]* and stimulates the ovaries to produce hormones/oestrogen *[1 mark]*.
2.4 oestrogen *[1 mark]*

Pages 64-65 — Controlling Fertility

Warm-up

Hormonal	Non-hormonal
contraceptive injection plastic intrauterine device contraceptive patch	abstinence condom diaphragm sterilisation

1.1 As a tablet taken by mouth. *[1 mark]*
1.2 The hormones inhibit FSH production *[1 mark]*.
1.3 progesterone *[1 mark]*
1.4 It stops the maturation/release of eggs. / It makes it hard for sperm to swim to the egg. / It stops any fertilised egg implanting in the uterus. *[1 mark]*
2.1 condom *[1 mark]*
2.2 female condom / diaphragm *[1 mark]*
2.3 They prevent the sperm reaching an egg *[1 mark]*.
2.4 spermicidal agents / spermicides *[1 mark]*
2.5 Avoiding intercourse when the woman is at the most fertile point in her menstrual cycle *[1 mark]*.
2.6 sterilisation *[1 mark]*
2.7 condom *[1 mark]*
3.1 E.g. the woman does not have to remember to take the contraceptive every day *[1 mark]*.
3.2 E.g. the injection lasts for several months, so if she has any side effects they may last for a long time *[1 mark]*.
3.3 E.g. barrier methods do not have the possible side effects associated with taking hormones *[1 mark]*.

Page 66 — More on Controlling Fertility

1.1 FSH is needed to stimulate eggs to mature. / No eggs would be released so the woman would not be able to become pregnant. *[1 mark]*
1.2 Luteinising hormone / LH *[1 mark]* because it stimulates the release of an egg *[1 mark]*.
1.3 Advantage: e.g. the woman may become pregnant naturally / without needing IVF *[1 mark]*.
Disadvantage: e.g. some women need several treatments so it can be expensive. / Too many eggs may be stimulated resulting in unexpected multiple pregnancies. *[1 mark]*
2.1 The mother is given FSH and LH *[1 mark]* to stimulate the maturation of several eggs *[1 mark]*. Several eggs are collected from the mother and fertilised by sperm from the father in a laboratory *[1 mark]*. The fertilised eggs are grown into embryos in the laboratory *[1 mark]*. At the stage when they are tiny balls of cells, one or two embryos are inserted into the mother's uterus *[1 mark]*.
2.2 Any two from: e.g. the treatment may not work so repeated attempts are needed, which could be upsetting/stressful for the couple. / It can result in multiple births which can be a risk to the mother's health. / The mother may have a strong reaction to the hormones (e.g. pain, vomiting). *[2 marks]*

Page 67 — Adrenaline and Thyroxine

Warm-up

Clockwise from top left: high, inhibited, normal, stimulated, low.
1.1 Thyroxine regulates basal metabolic rate *[1 mark]*.
1.2 thyroid gland *[1 mark]*
2.1 adrenal glands *[1 mark]*
2.2 E.g. it increases heart rate *[1 mark]*, which boosts the delivery of oxygen to the brain and muscles *[1 mark]* and also boosts the delivery of glucose to the brain and muscles *[1 mark]*.
2.3 flight or fight *[1 mark]*

Topic B6 — Inheritance, Variation and Evolution

Page 68 — DNA

1.1 DNA is located in the nucleus of animal and plant cells *[1 mark]*.
1.2 The structures that contain DNA *[1 mark]*.
2.1 Genes code for particular sequences of amino acids *[1 mark]*, which are put together to make specific proteins *[1 mark]*.
2.2 The entire set of genetic material in an organism *[1 mark]*.
2.3 E.g. it allows scientists to identify genes that are linked to different types of diseases *[1 mark]*. Knowing which genes are linked to inherited diseases could help us to develop effective treatments for them *[1 mark]*.

Page 69 — Reproduction

1.1 sperm *[1 mark]*
1.2 egg (cell) *[1 mark]*
1.3 meiosis *[1 mark]*
1.4 clones *[1 mark]*
1.5 mitosis *[1 mark]*
2.1 Because gametes only have half the number of chromosomes of a normal cell *[1 mark]*, so when two gametes fuse together the fertilised egg cell has the full number of chromosomes *[1 mark]*.
2.2 Any four from: e.g. asexual reproduction only involves one parent, whereas sexual reproduction involves two. / Unlike in sexual reproduction, there is no fusion of gametes in asexual reproduction. / Unlike in sexual reproduction, there is no mixing of chromosomes in asexual reproduction. / Unlike sexual reproduction, asexual reproduction doesn't give rise to genetic variation (as the offspring are genetically identical to the parent). / Asexual reproduction doesn't involve meiosis, whereas sexual reproduction does. *[4 marks — 1 mark for each correct answer.]*

Page 70 — Meiosis

1.1 In the reproductive organs / ovaries and testes *[1 mark]*.
1.2 It is duplicated *[1 mark]*.
1.3 two *[1 mark]*
1.4 Four gametes are produced *[1 mark]*, each with only a single set of chromosomes *[1 mark]*. Each of the gametes is genetically different from the others *[1 mark]*.

2.1 two *[1 mark]*
2.2 mitosis *[1 mark]*
2.3 They differentiate into different types of specialised cell *[1 mark]*.

Page 71 — X and Y Chromosomes

1.1 23 pairs of chromosomes *[1 mark]*
1.2

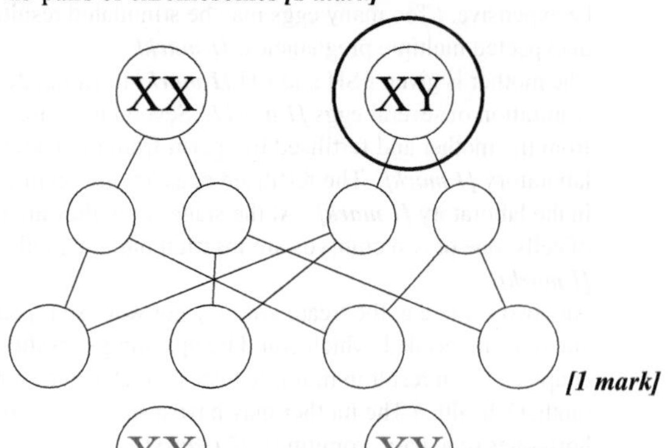

[1 mark]

1.3

[1 mark for all gametes correct]

1.4

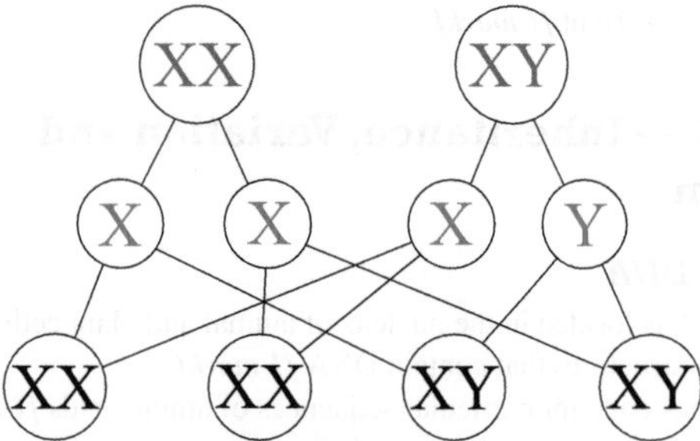

[1 mark if all the offspring genotypes are correct]

1.5 50:50 / 1:1 *[1 mark]*
1.6 E.g.

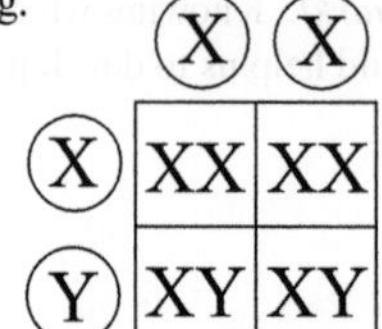

[1 mark for correct gametes of parents, 1 mark for correct genotypes of offspring.]

Pages 72-73 — Genetic Diagrams

Warm-up
alleles, recessive, homozygous, heterozygous, a single gene, multiple genes

1.1 Because there are carriers who don't have the disease *[1 mark]*.
1.2

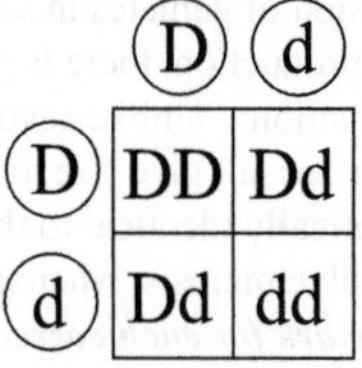

probability = **25%**

[1 mark for correct genotypes of parents, 1 mark if all gametes are correct, 1 mark if all offspring genotypes are correct, 1 mark for correct probability.]

2.1 3:1 *[1 mark]*
2.2

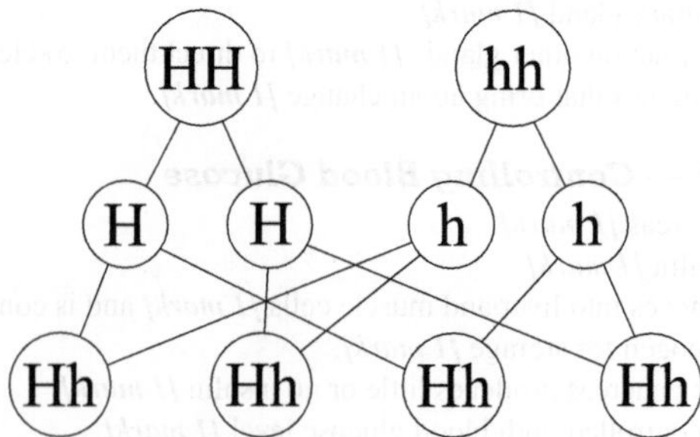

number of long-haired puppies = **8**

[1 mark for correct gametes, 1 mark for correct offspring genotypes, 1 mark for correct number of long-haired puppies.]

2.3 E.g.

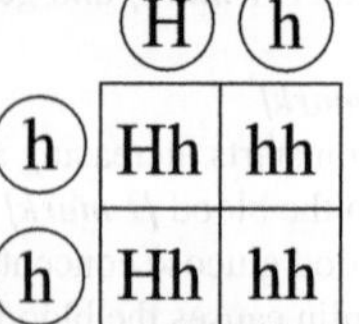

ratio = **1:1**

[1 mark if all gametes are correct, 1 mark if all offspring genotypes are correct, 1 mark for correct probability.]

Page 74 — Inherited Disorders

1.1 Being born with extra fingers or toes *[1 mark]*.
1.2 That the allele for polydactyly is dominant *[1 mark]*.
1.3 Because the allele for cystic fibrosis is recessive *[1 mark]*, so the offspring must have two copies of the allele to have the disorder *[1 mark]*. There is only a 1 in 4 chance of this occurring when each parent has one copy of the allele *[1 mark]*.
2.1 E.g. it implies that people with genetic problems are undesirable, which could increase prejudice *[1 mark]*. Screening is expensive *[1 mark]*. There could become a point where everyone wants to screen their embryo in IVF to pick the most desirable one *[1 mark]*.
2.2 E.g. it will help to stop people suffering from genetic disorders *[1 mark]*. Treating disorders costs the government and taxpayer a lot of money. Screening to reduce the number of people with disorders could save money *[1 mark]*. Parents cannot use it to select desirable characteristics for their baby, as there are laws to stop screening going too far *[1 mark]*.

Page 75 — Variation

1.1 genetic *[1 mark]*
1.2 environmental *[1 mark]*
2 The mutation could lead to a new phenotype *[1 mark]*. If the environment changes, the new phenotype could make the individual more suited to the new environment *[1 mark]*. It could then become common throughout the species relatively quickly by natural selection *[1 mark]*.

Page 76— Evolution

1 The environment changes too quickly *[1 mark]*. A new predator kills them all *[1 mark]*. A new disease kills them all *[1 mark]*. They can't compete with another new species for food *[1 mark]*. A catastrophic event occurs that kills them all *[1 mark]*.
2 Species show a wide variation in their characteristics because of differences in their alleles/genes *[1 mark]*. In this case, hares with smaller ears have more suitable characteristics for a cold environment because they will lose less heat *[1 mark]*, so are more likely to survive and successfully reproduce *[1 mark]* and pass on the genes controlling smaller ears to the next generation/their offspring *[1 mark]*. Over time, these genes will have become more common in the species, causing the hares to evolve *[1 mark]*.

Page 77 — Selective Breeding

1.1 Artificial selection *[1 mark]*
1.2 The breeding of organisms so that the genes for particular useful or attractive characteristics stay in the population *[1 mark]*.
1.3 To produce cows that produce lots of milk/have a high milk yield *[1 mark]*.
2.1 How to grade your answer:
Level 0: There is no relevant information. *[No marks]*

Level 1: There are some relevant points describing selective breeding but the answer is missing some detail. ***[1 to 2 marks]***

Level 2: There is a clear, detailed description of selective breeding that explains how dogs can be selectively bred for good, gentle temperament. ***[3 to 4 marks]***

Here are some points your answer may include:
He could have selected two individuals from the population with the best temperaments.
These two individuals would have been bred together.
He would then have selected the individuals from the offspring with the best temperaments and bred them together.
He would have repeated this process over several generations.
This would make the good temperament trait become stronger over time.
Eventually all the puppies would have the good, gentle temperament trait.

2.2 Because selective breeding leads to there being a reduced number of different alleles in the population / a reduced gene pool ***[1 mark]***, so there's more chance of the puppies inheriting a genetic defect if it's present in the population ***[1 mark]***.

2.3 There is less variation in a selectively bred population ***[1 mark]***, so there's less chance of there being any alleles in the population that would give the puppies resistance to the disease ***[1 mark]***, so if one individual gets the disease, the others are also likely to succumb to it ***[1 mark]***.

Pages 78-79 — Genetic Engineering

Warm-up

False, False, True, True

1.1 The transfer of a gene responsible for a desirable characteristic ***[1 mark]*** from one organism's genome into another organism's genome ***[1 mark]***.

1.2 Enzyme are used to isolate/cut the desired gene from the organism's genome ***[1 mark]***.

1.3 The gene is first inserted into a vector ***[1 mark]***. The vector is then introduced to the target organism ***[1 mark]*** and this inserts the gene into the organism's cells so that the organism develops with the desired characteristic ***[1 mark]***.

1.4 Any two from: e.g. bacteria have been genetically engineered to produce human insulin that can be used to treat diabetes. / Sheep have been genetically engineered to produce drugs in their milk that can treat human diseases. / Scientists are researching genetic modification treatments (gene therapy) for inherited diseases caused by faulty genes ***[2 marks — 1 mark for each correct answer.]***.

2.1 genetically modified ***[1 mark]***

2.2 Any two from: e.g. to make them resistant to herbicides. / To make them resistant to disease. / To make them resistant to insects. ***[2 marks — 1 mark for each correct answer.]***.

2.3 Mean fruit circumference of Plant 1 =
$(16.4 + 16.8 + 15.9 + 16.2 + 15.7 + 16.4 + 16.3 + 16.0 + 15.9 + 16.0) \div 10 =$ **16.2 cm (3 s.f.)** ***[1 mark]***
Mean fruit circumference of Plant 2 =
$(20.2 + 20.4 + 19.8 + 19.6 + 20.4 + 20.6 + 20.2 + 19.9 + 20.1 + 20.0) \div 10 =$ **20.1 cm (3 s.f.)** ***[1 mark]***

2.4 $20.1 - 16.2 = 3.9$ cm
$(3.9 \div 16.2) \times 100 =$ **24.1% (3 s.f.)**
[1 mark for correct working, 1 mark for correct answer.]

To calculate percentage change, you first need to work out the difference between the two figures. You then need calculate what percentage that difference is of the first figure.

2.5 Any one from: e.g. some people say that growing GM crops will affect the number of wild flowers, and so the population of insects, that live in and around the crops — reducing farmland biodiversity. / Some people are concerned that we might not fully understand the effects of eating GM crops on human health. / People are concerned that transplanted genes might get out into the natural environment. ***[1 mark]***

Page 80 — Fossils

Warm-up

False, True, True

1.1 Because decay microbes can't survive in the sap or amber ***[1 mark]*** as there isn't any oxygen or moisture ***[1 mark]***.

1.2 From gradual replacement of parts of an organism by minerals ***[1 mark]***. From the preserved casts and impressions of things like burrows/footprints/rootlet traces in a soft material (like clay) ***[1 mark]***.

1.3 Many early life-forms were soft bodied and decayed completely, without forming fossils ***[1 mark]***. Fossils that did form may have been destroyed by geological activity ***[1 mark]***. This means that the fossil record is incomplete ***[1 mark]***.

Pages 81-82 — Antibiotic-Resistant Bacteria

1.1 E.g when they are prescribed for viral infections ***[1 mark]*** or non-serious conditions ***[1 mark]***.

1.2 Because this ensures that all bacteria are destroyed ***[1 mark]***, so there are none left to mutate ***[1 mark]*** and develop into antibiotic-resistant strains ***[1 mark]***.

2.1 Because the rate of development of new antibiotics is slow ***[1 mark]*** and it is a costly process ***[1 mark]***.

2.2 Bacteria develop random mutations in their DNA ***[1 mark]***, some of which lead to the bacteria becoming less affected by antibiotics ***[1 mark]***. These bacteria are better able to survive and reproduce in hosts undergoing antibiotic treatment ***[1 mark]***, meaning that the gene becomes more common in the population, forming antibiotic-resistant strains ***[1 mark]***. As there is no effective treatment for these strains, they can spread very easily between individuals ***[1 mark]***.

3.1 How to grade your answer:

Level 0: There is no relevant information. ***[No marks]***

Level 1: There is a brief description of a method that could be used to carry out the investigation. Very little detail is included and some steps may be in the wrong order. ***[1 to 2 marks]***

Level 2: There is a good description of a method that could be used to carry out the investigation. Some detail is missing, but all of the steps are in a sensible order. ***[3 to 4 marks]***

Level 3: There is a clear and detailed description of a method that could be used to carry out the investigation. All of the steps are in a sensible order. ***[5 to 6 marks]***

Here are some points your answer may include:
Use a sterile pipette to measure out equal volumes of sterile nutrient broth solution into four sterile glass bottles.
Use another sterile pipette to add equal volumes of ampicillin solution to two of the glass bottles.
Use another sterile pipette to transfer some of strain A to one bottle with ampicillin in it and one bottle without ampicillin.
Use another sterile pipette to transfer some of strain B to one bottle with ampicillin and one bottle without ampicillin.
Set up a control experiment without bacteria / just broth solution and the antibiotic.
Put lids on all of the bottles. Store them all at the same temperature for a few days.
Observe each bottle to see if the nutrient broth solution has gone cloudy.

3.2 E.g. if strain B is resistant to ampicillin, it may cause bacterial infections that are difficult to treat if it is released into the general population, so it must be disposed of properly. / The bacteria used may pose a health risk to humans if not disposed of properly. / If the antibiotic used is not disposed of properly it may be released into the environment, where other bacteria may develop resistance to it ***[1 mark]***.

Page 83 — Classification

1.1 E.g. current classification data ***[1 mark]*** and information from the fossil record ***[1 mark]***.

1.2 B ***[1 mark]***

1.3 G and H ***[1 mark]***

2.1 kingdom, phylum, class, order, family, genus, species ***[1 mark]***

2.2 (Carl) Woese ***[1 mark]***

2.3 plants ***[1 mark]***, animals ***[1 mark]***, protists ***[1 mark]***

Topic B7 — Ecology

Page 84 — Competition

1.1 the soil *[1 mark]*
1.2 light *[1 mark]* and space *[1 mark]*
1.3 Any three from: space/territory / food / water / mates *[3 marks]*
2.1 interdependence *[1 mark]*
2.2 E.g. the number of blue tits might decrease *[1 mark]* because there would be no caterpillars for them to eat *[1 mark]*. The numbers of plants might increase *[1 mark]* because there would be no caterpillars to eat them *[1 mark]*.
2.3 A stable community is one where all the species and environmental factors are in balance *[1 mark]* so that the population sizes remain fairly constant *[1 mark]*.

Pages 85-86 — Abiotic and Biotic Factors

1.1 Light intensity, temperature and carbon dioxide level are all examples of abiotic factors. *[1 mark]*

The other answers are incorrect because they mix up examples of biotic and abiotic factors. Remember, abiotic factors are non-living factors and biotic factors are living factors.

1.2 E.g. oxygen level *[1 mark]*
1.3 Any two from: e.g. moisture level / soil pH / soil mineral content / carbon dioxide level *[2 marks]*
2 E.g. because the grey and red squirrels were in competition *[1 mark]* for the same resources such as food and shelter *[1 mark]*. The grey squirrels out-competed the red squirrels *[1 mark]*.
3 The birds would not be feeding on the insects *[1 mark]*, so insects would breed and increase in numbers *[1 mark]*. More insects would eat more grass so the grass plant numbers might decrease *[1 mark]*.
4.1 Both populations increase then decrease sharply, then increase again over the ten years *[1 mark]*. The heron population starts to decrease and increase slightly later than the perch population *[1 mark]*.
4.2 The average pH of the lake fell between years 4 and 5 *[1 mark]*. Possibly not all of the perch could survive in the more acidic water *[1 mark]*. The data cannot confirm the reason because there might have been another abiotic or biotic factor that affected the perch population *[1 mark]*.

You still get the second mark here if you came up with any other sensible reason why the fall in the pH of the water might have caused the perch population to decrease.

4.3 E.g. there might be other fish/prey in the lake, which aren't affected by the disease, that the herons can eat *[1 mark]*. The other fish/prey might have more food if the perch population falls, so their populations will increase *[1 mark]*. So the herons might still have as much food as before *[1 mark]*.

Pages 87-88 — Adaptations

1.1 extremophiles *[1 mark]*
1.2 bacteria *[1 mark]*
1.3 high pressure *[1 mark]*
2.1 Long eyelashes stop sand getting into the eyes *[1 mark]*. Large feet stop the camel sinking into the sand / make it easier for the camel to walk in sand *[1 mark]*.
2.2 It reduces water loss *[1 mark]*.
2.3 A swollen stem stores water *[1 mark]*.
2.4 Shallow, wide-spreading roots allow water to be absorbed over a larger area *[1 mark]* while long, deep roots allow the plant to absorb water from deep below the surface *[1 mark]*.
3.1 E.g. they would seek shade *[1 mark]*.
3.2 dark coloured skin *[1 mark]*
3.3 functional adaptation *[1 mark]*

Page 89 — Food Chains

Warm-up

producer — seaweed, secondary consumer — shark

1.1 primary consumer *[1 mark]*
1.2 They produce glucose *[1 mark]* by carrying out photosynthesis *[1 mark]*. They then use this glucose to make biological molecules that make up the plant's biomass *[1 mark]*.
2.1 The number of lynx increases *[1 mark]* because the number of snowshoe hares is increasing and so they have lots of food *[1 mark]*.
2.2 An increase in the number of lynx, which mean more hares are eaten *[1 mark]*.

Page 90 — Using Quadrats

1.1 It avoids the data being biased *[1 mark]*.
1.2 13 buttercups *[1 mark]*
1.3 15.5 buttercups *[1 mark]*
1.4 $(15 + 13 + 16 + 23 + 26 + 23 + 13 + 12 + 16 + 13) \div 10 = 170 \div 10 =$ **17 buttercups per 0.5 m^2** *[1 mark]*
1.5 Mean number of buttercups per m^2 = $17 \times 2 = 34$
Estimated population size = mean number of buttercups per m^2 × total area of the field in m^2
Estimated population size = 34×1750
= **59 500 buttercups** ***[3 marks for correct answer, otherwise 1 mark for '34 buttercups per m^2' and 1 mark for '34 × 1750'.]***

Pages 91-92 — Using Transects

1.1 Zones B and C. *[1 mark]*
1.2 long grass *[1 mark]*
1.3 Zone A is closest to the pond where the soil has more moisture *[1 mark]*. Zone A also has a higher light intensity *[1 mark]*.
1.4 Zone B *[1 mark]* because only short grass grows in zone B *[1 mark]*.
1.5 The light levels may be too low. / The moisture level may be too low. *[1 mark]*
1.6 Record the number of times each of the four species touch the transect line. / Count the number of species/measure the percentage cover of each species using a quadrat placed along the transect. *[1 mark]*
2.1 E.g. the ground might be slippery / there might be large waves from the sea / the tide might come in *[1 mark]*.

Any sensible suggestion of a hazard you might find at a beach would get you the mark for this question.

2.2 Advantage: e.g. you can cover a larger distance in the same amount of time / it takes less time to collect data from along the transect *[1 mark]*.
Disadvantage: e.g. the results might not be as accurate / some species might get missed *[1 mark]*.
2.3 The percentage cover of bladderwrack increases between 2 m and 18 m from the low tide point / the further the distance from the low tide point, the higher the percentage cover of bladderwrack, up to 18 m *[1 mark]*. The percentage cover then falls between 18 m and 20 m *[1 mark]*.
2.4 E.g. they could measure the salt concentration of the water around the bladderwrack at each interval *[1 mark]*.

Page 93 — The Water Cycle

Warm-up

evaporate, water vapour, cools, precipitation

1.1 evaporation *[1 mark]*
1.2 Precipitation is water that falls from the clouds *[1 mark]*.
1.3 It provides fresh water for plants and animals *[1 mark]*.

Page 94 — The Carbon Cycle

1.1 photosynthesis *[1 mark]*
1.2 (green) plants *[1 mark]*
1.3 burning *[1 mark]*
1.4 Any one from: e.g. leather / wool. *[1 mark]*
1.5 Carbon dioxide is returned back to the atmosphere *[1 mark]* when the microorganisms involved in decay respire *[1 mark]*.

Pages 95-96 — Biodiversity and Waste Management

1.1 The variety of different species of organisms on Earth, or within an ecosystem. *[1 mark]*
1.2 E.g. deforestation / waste production *[1 mark]*
2.1 The human population is growing *[1 mark]* and the standard of living is increasing *[1 mark]*.
2.2 Any two from: e.g. sewage / toxic chemicals / fertilisers / pesticides / herbicides *[2 marks]*
2.3 E.g. smoke *[1 mark]* and acidic gases *[1 mark]*.
3.1 It reduces the variety of plants on the land (by killing the weeds)

[1 mark] and it may kill plants and animals if it is washed into nearby water / it pollutes nearby water *[1 mark]*.

3.2 Because all the different species in the ecosystem depend on each other (e.g. for shelter and food) *[1 mark]*. Different species can also help to maintain the right physical environment for each other *[1 mark]*.

4.1 River 2 has a higher level of water pollution than River 1 *[1 mark]*. River 2 contains more rat-tailed maggots than River 1, and these are found in highly polluted water *[1 mark]*. River 2 also contains fewer freshwater shrimp and water lice than River 1, and these are found in water with a medium or low level of pollution *[1 mark]*.

You'd also get the marks here for explaining this the other way round — for describing how you can tell that River 1 has a lower level of pollution than River 2.

4.2 The student would need to survey one area that is just downstream of the discharge site, which will be affected by the waste water *[1 mark]*, and one area that is just upstream of the discharge site, where no waste water is present *[1 mark]*. Then the student can compare the populations of the indicator species present at both sites to assess the water pollution levels *[1 mark]*.

Page 97 — Global Warming

Warm-up

the Sun, space, gases, increases

1.1 carbon dioxide and methane *[1 mark]*

1.2 Higher temperatures could cause seawater to expand / ice to melt *[1 mark]*, which could cause the sea level to rise above low-lying land *[1 mark]*.

1.3 Any two from: e.g. changes in the distribution of species where temperature/rainfall has changed. / Changes to the migration pattern of some animals. / Reduction in biodiversity as some species become extinct.
[2 marks — 1 mark for each correct answer.]

Page 98 — Deforestation and Land Use

1 Any two from: e.g. building / farming / quarrying / dumping waste *[2 marks — 1 mark for each correct answer]*.

2.1 E.g. to use the land as farmland. / To use the peat as compost. *[1 mark]*

2.2 Carbon dioxide is released *[1 mark]*, which contributes to global warming *[1 mark]*.

2.3 It reduces biodiversity *[1 mark]* because it destroys habitats / reduces the area of habitats *[1 mark]*.

3.1 To clear land to grow the crops needed to produce biofuels *[1 mark]*.

3.2 E.g. to provide land for cattle (to raise for food) *[1 mark]*. To provide land to grow crops, e.g. rice (to provide more food) *[1 mark]*.

4 Any two from: e.g. it increases the amount of carbon dioxide in the atmosphere *[1 mark]* because carbon dioxide is released by burning wood and the decomposing of wood by microorganisms *[1 mark]*. / It reduces the rate at which carbon dioxide is removed from the atmosphere *[1 mark]* because there are fewer trees taking it up for photosynthesis *[1 mark]*. / It leads to a reduction in biodiversity in the area *[1 mark]* because trees/habitats are destroyed *[1 mark]*.

Page 99 — Maintaining Ecosystems and Biodiversity

1.1 Burning fewer fossil fuels. *[1 mark]*

1.2 E.g. this could reduce the amount of land taken over for landfill *[1 mark]*, leaving ecosystems in place *[1 mark]*.

2.1 It decreases biodiversity *[1 mark]*, because the habitat wouldn't be able to support a wide range of organisms *[1 mark]*.

2.2 The strips of grassland and hedgerows increase the biodiversity by providing more habitats / food sources *[1 mark]*.

3 E.g. it costs money to protect biodiversity (and make sure that the programmes are being followed) and some people may feel that the money should be spent on other things *[1 mark]*. Protecting biodiversity may have a negative impact on local people's livelihood (e.g. if they're employed in tree-felling), which could affect the local economy *[1 mark]*. Some people (e.g. farmers) may want to kill organisms that are regarded as pests to protect crops and livestock *[1 mark]*. Some people may want to use land for new housing or agricultural land *[1 mark]*.

Topic C1 — Atomic Structure and the Periodic Table

Page 100 — Atoms

Warm-up

The radius of an atom is approximately **0.1** nanometres.
The radius of the nucleus is around $\mathbf{1 \times 10^{-14}}$ metres.
That's about **1/10 000** of the radius of an atom.
An atom doesn't have an overall **charge** as it has equal numbers of **protons/electrons** and **electrons/protons**.

1.1 nucleus *[1 mark]*

1.2 –1 *[1 mark]*

1.3 neutron: 0 charge *[1 mark]*
proton: +1 charge *[1 mark]*

2.1 mass number = 39 *[1 mark]*

2.2 atomic number = 19 *[1 mark]*

2.3 protons = 19 *[1 mark]*
neutrons = mass number – atomic number
= 39 – 19 = **20** *[1 mark]*
electrons = 19 *[1 mark]*

Page 101 — Elements

1.1 Atoms are the smallest part of an element that can exist *[1 mark]*.

1.2 They have the same number of protons / 17 protons *[1 mark]* but a different number of neutrons / ${}^{35}_{17}Cl$ has 2 less neutrons than ${}^{37}_{17}Cl$ *[1 mark]*.

2.1

Isotope	No. of Protons	No. of Neutrons	No. of Electrons
${}^{32}S$	16	16	16
${}^{33}S$	16	17	16
${}^{34}S$	16	18	16
${}^{36}S$	16	20	16

[3 marks — 1 mark for each correct column]

2.2 Relative atomic mass = [(94.99 × 32) + (0.75 × 33) + (4.25 × 34) + (0.01 × 36)] ÷ (94.99 + 0.75 + 4.25 + 0.01)
= 3209.29 ÷ 100 = 32.0929 = **32.1** *[2 marks for correct answer, otherwise one mark for using correct equation]*

2.3 X and Z are isotopes *[1 mark]*. They have the same atomic number / same number of protons *[1 mark]* but different mass numbers / number of neutrons *[1 mark]*.

Page 102 — Compounds

1.1 It contains two elements chemically combined *[1 mark]*.

1.2 4 *[1 mark]*

A molecule of ammonia contains 1 nitrogen atom and 3 hydrogen atoms making a total of 4 atoms altogether.

2.1 sodium chloride *[1 mark]*

2.2 Any one of: **B.** NaCl / **C.** C_2H_4 / **E.** H_2O *[1 mark]*
It contains two or more elements chemically combined (in fixed proportions) *[1 mark]*.

2.3 6 *[1 mark]*

C_2H_4 contains 2 carbon atoms and 4 hydrogen atoms.

2.4 Yes, a new compound has been made as the atoms in C_2H_6 are in different proportions to the atoms in C or F / there are a different number of hydrogen atoms in the molecule *[1 mark]*.

Page 103 — Chemical Equations

Warm-up

1 True

2 False

3 True

4 True

1.1 sodium + chlorine → sodium chloride *[1 mark]*

1.2 $2Na + Cl_2 \rightarrow 2NaCl$ *[1 mark]*

2.1 $\mathbf{4}NH_3 + \mathbf{5}O_2 \rightarrow \mathbf{4}NO + \mathbf{6}H_2O$ /
$\mathbf{2}NH_3 + \mathbf{2.5}O_2 \rightarrow \mathbf{2}NO + \mathbf{3}H_2O$ *[1 mark]*

2.2 E.g. there are 7 oxygen atoms on the left hand side of the equation and only 6 on the right hand side *[1 mark]*.

Page 104 — Mixtures and Chromatography

1.1 Mixture *[1 mark]*. Air consists of two or more elements or compounds *[1 mark]* that aren't chemically combined together *[1 mark]*.

1.2 No *[1 mark]*, as argon is an element in a mixture. Chemical properties are not affected by being in a mixture *[1 mark]*.

2 How to grade your answer:
Level 0: Nothing written worthy of credit *[No marks]*.
Level 1: Some explanation or description given but little detail and key information missing *[1–2 marks]*.
Level 2: Clear description of method and some explanation of results but some detail missing *[3–4 marks]*.
Level 3: A clear and detailed description of method and a full explanation of results *[5–6 marks]*.
Here are some points your answer may include:
Setting up the experiment
Draw a line in pencil near the bottom of a piece of chromatography paper.
Place a small sample of each ink on the pencil line.
Pour a shallow layer of water / solvent into a beaker.
Place the chromatography paper in the container.
The water should be below the pencil line and the ink spots.
Place a lid on the container and wait for the solvent to rise to near the top of the paper.
Remove the paper from the container when the solvent has risen close to the top of the paper.
Explanation of results
A shows one spot, so only contains one dye.
B shows two spots that have separated, so contains two dyes.
C shows three spots that have separated, so contains three dyes.
B and C are mixtures as they contain more than one element or compound not chemically combined together.
B and C contain at least one of the same dyes

Page 105 — More Separation Techniques

1.1 Add water to the mixture to dissolve the potassium chloride *[1 mark]*. Filter the mixture. The chalk will stay on the filter paper, *[1 mark]* the dissolved potassium chloride will pass through *[1 mark]*.

1.2 E.g. evaporate the potassium chloride solution to a much smaller volume and then leave it to cool *[1 mark]*.

2.1 Add the mixture to methylbenzene. The sulfur will dissolve (the iron will not dissolve) *[1 mark]*. Filter the solution to obtain the insoluble iron *[1 mark]*. Evaporate the methylbenzene to obtain crystals of sulfur *[1 mark]*.

2.2 No, the student is incorrect *[1 mark]*. The iron and sulfur are chemically combined in iron(II) sulfide / iron(II) sulfide is a compound *[1 mark]* so chemical methods would be needed to separate them out *[1 mark]*.

Pages 106-107 — Distillation

1 Simple distillation *[1 mark]*

2.1 Place a stopper / stopper with a thermometer in the top of the distillation flask *[1 mark]*.

2.2 The solution is heated/boiled and the octane evaporates first as it has a lower boiling point than the impurity *[1 mark]*. There is cold water flowing through the (Liebig) condenser *[1 mark]*. This condenses the gaseous octane back into a liquid which is then collected *[1 mark]*.

2.3 The octane has a boiling point greater than 100 °C / greater than the boiling point of water *[1 mark]*. So it would not evaporate *[1 mark]*.

3.1 In the first step, the temperature that the student heated the solution to was too high *[1 mark]*. Heating the mixture to 120 °C will cause both the ethanol and the water to evaporate, leaving a mixture of both salts in the flask *[1 mark]*.

3.2 The student should heat the mixture to a temperature of 78 °C. This will cause the ethanol in the mixture to evaporate, but not the water *[1 mark]*.

3.3 Ethanol is a flammable solvent so the mixture could catch fire if there is a lot left in the solution *[1 mark]*.

3.4 Gently heat the solution in an evaporating dish until some of the liquid has evaporated, according to the student's method. When crystals start to form, remove the dish from the heat and leave to cool *[1 mark]*. Filter the crystals out of the solution and leave to dry in a warm place *[1 mark]*.

Pages 108-109 — The History of The Atom

Warm-up
New experimental evidence can disprove models — **True**
Scientific models can be based on existing theories and new experimental evidence — **True**
Older scientific theories must be ignored when new ones are adopted — **False**

1.1 Tiny solid spheres that can't be divided *[1 mark]*.

1.2 Plum pudding model — A positively charged 'ball' with negatively charged electrons in it *[1 mark]*.
Bohr's model — Electrons in fixed orbits surrounding a small positively charged nucleus *[1 mark]*.
Rutherford's nuclear model — A small positively charged nucleus surrounded by a 'cloud' of negative electrons *[1 mark]*.

1.3 neutron *[1 mark]*

2.1 Most of the atom is "empty" space *[1 mark]*.

2.2 Niels Bohr *[1 mark]*

3.1 Atoms are neutral / have no overall charge *[1 mark]*. Therefore there must have been positive charge to balance the negative charge of the electrons *[1 mark]*.

3.2 How to grade your answer:
Level 0: Nothing written worthy of credit *[No marks]*.
Level 1: A brief description of either the nuclear or the 'plum pudding' model is given *[1 to 2 marks]*.
Level 2: A description of both the nuclear model and the plum pudding model is given and some comparisons made *[3 to 4 marks]*.
Level 3: A full comparison of the models is given and similarities and differences are clearly explained *[5 to 6 marks]*.
Here are some points your answer may include:
Similarities
They both have areas of positive charge.
They both have electrons.
They are both neutral overall.
Differences
Positive charge isn't divided into protons in plum pudding model.
Plum pudding model does not have a nucleus but has a 'ball' of positive charge instead.
Plum pudding model does not have neutrons or protons, it only has electrons surrounded by a positive charge.
Plum pudding model does not have shells of electrons (surrounding nucleus), the electrons are arranged randomly within a sphere of positive charge.
Modern nuclear model has most of the mass concentrated in the nucleus but the plum pudding model has the mass spread evenly throughout the entire atom.

Page 110 — Electronic Structure

1.1 2,8,8,2 *[1 mark]*

1.2 The electrons in an atom occupy the lowest energy levels/ innermost shell first *[1 mark]*. The innermost shell/lowest energy level can hold 2 electrons *[1 mark]*.

2.1 Chlorine: 2,8,7 *[1 mark]*

2.2 S

[1 mark for correct number of electrons, 1 mark for correct arrangement]

You don't have to have the electrons paired up on the diagram. As long as there is the same number of electrons on the same shells you get the marks.

2.3 Phosphorus/P *[1 mark]*

Page 111 — Development of The Periodic Table

1.1 He left gaps so that elements with similar properties were in the same group / for elements that had not yet been discovered ***[1 mark]***.

1.2 **D**. Between 2.4 and 7.2 g/cm^3 ***[1 mark]***. **E**. EkO_2 ***[1 mark]*** **F**. $EkCl_4$ ***[1 mark]*** **G**. Very slow ***[1 mark]***.

2.1 Protons (neutrons and electrons) had not been discovered / atomic numbers weren't known ***[1 mark]***.

2.2 Ar and K / Te and I ***[1 mark]***.

2.3 Isotopes of an element have different numbers of neutrons/ different atomic masses ***[1 mark]***, but the same chemical properties ***[1 mark]***.

Page 112 — The Modern Periodic Table

1.1 By atomic number / proton number ***[1 mark]***.

1.2 Similar properties occur at regular intervals / there are repeating patterns in the properties of the elements ***[1 mark]***.

1.3 They have the same number of outer shell electrons ***[1 mark]***.

2.1 Group 2 ***[1 mark]***. The atom has 2 outer shell electrons. ***[1 mark]***.

2.2 Period 3 ***[1 mark]***. The atom has 3 shells of electrons ***[1 mark]***.

2.3 Magnesium/Mg ***[1 mark]***

2.4 Choose one from: beryllium / calcium / strontium / barium / radium ***[1 mark]***

Page 113 — Metals and Non-Metals

1.1 A^{2+}: metal X^{2-}: non-metal ***[1 mark if both correct.]***

1.2 Any three from, e.g.: dull / brittle / poor conductor of electricity / low density / lower melting point/boiling point than metals
[1 mark for each].

2.1 Metals: Towards the left and bottom.
Non-metals: Towards the right and top ***[1 mark]***.

2.2 Elements that react to form positive ions are metals ***[1 mark]***.

2.3 Any one from: e.g. good electrical conductor / good thermal conductor / strong / high boiling point / high melting point / malleable ***[1 mark]***.

2.4 Both are metals that lose their (2 or 3) outer shell electrons ***[1 mark]*** to form positive ions ***[1 mark]***.

Page 114 — Group 1 Elements

1.1 **Y** ***[1 mark]***. As element **Y** has a higher melting point, it must be higher up the group than **X** ***[1 mark]***.

The higher up the group an element is, the lower its atomic number.

1.2 $2X_{(s)} + 2H_2O_{(l)} \rightarrow 2XOH_{(aq)} + H_{2(g)}$
[1 mark for correct reactants and products and 1 mark for balanced equation. Half the ratio is acceptable]

1.3 Anything between 8-14 ***[1 mark]***.

2.1

	Boiling Point / °C	Radius of atom / pm
Rb	687.8	248
Cs	670.8	265
Fr	**Accept lower than 670.8**	**Accept greater than 265**

[1 mark for each correct answer]

2.2 Francium would be more reactive than caesium ***[1 mark]***. As you go further down the group the outer electron is further away from the nucleus ***[1 mark]***, so the attraction between the nucleus and the electron decreases and the electron is more easily lost ***[1 mark]***.

2.3 Formula: Fr_3P ***[1 mark]***
Equation: $12Fr + P_4 \rightarrow 4Fr_3P$ ***[1 mark for correct reactants and products, 1 mark for correctly balancing the equation]***

Pages 115-116 — Group 7 Elements

Warm-up

Fluorine
Chlorine
Bromine
Iodine

1.1 They are non-metals that exist as molecules of two atoms ***[1 mark]***.

1.2 Chlorine is more reactive than bromine ***[1 mark]***. This is because chlorine's outer shell is closer to the nucleus ***[1 mark]*** so it's easier for chlorine to gain an electron when it reacts ***[1 mark]***.

Because of the increasing distance between the nucleus and the outer shell, reactivity decreases down the group. Bromine is further down the group than chlorine, it's outer shell is further away from the nucleus and therefore it's less reactive than chlorine.

1.3 P ***[1 mark]***

2.1 $2Fe + 3Br_2 \rightarrow 2FeBr_3$ ***[1 mark for Br_2 and 1 mark for balanced equation. Half the ratio is acceptable]***

2.2 –1 ***[1 mark]***

All halide ions form ions with a –1 charge.

3.1 chlorine + potassium bromide → **potassium chloride + bromine** ***[1 mark]***

3.2 The solution will turn orange ***[1 mark]***.

3.3 displacement ***[1 mark]***

3.4 No ***[1 mark]***, as chlorine is less reactive than fluorine ***[1 mark]***.

4.1 The halogens have seven electrons in their outer shell ***[1 mark]***. As you go further down the group additional shells are added so the outer electron is further away from the nucleus ***[1 mark]***.

4.2 Astatine will react more slowly than fluorine ***[1 mark]*** since reactivity decreases down the group ***[1 mark]***. Both astatine and fluorine have 7 outer shell electrons so react in a similar way ***[1 mark]***. So astatine will react with hydrogen to form hydrogen astatide/HAt ***[1 mark]***. $H_2 + At_2 \rightarrow 2HAt$ ***[1 mark]***

Page 117 — Group 0 Elements

1.1 Rn Boiling Point: Above –108 °C ***[1 mark]***, Xe Density: Between 0.0037 and 0.0097 ***[1 mark]***, Ar Atomic Radius: Less than 109 pm ***[1 mark]***.

1.2 Krypton is unreactive ***[1 mark]***. It has a stable electron arrangement / full outer shell / 8 electrons in its outer shell ***[1 mark]***.

1.3 Helium only has 2 electrons in its outer shell. The rest of the noble gases have 8 ***[1 mark]***.

2.1 Noble gases are unreactive / they have stable electron arrangements / full outer shells / 8 electrons in their outer shell ***[1 mark]***.

2.2 Iodine is much less reactive than fluorine ***[1 mark]***.

2.3 Neon solidified at –249 °C and xenon at –112 °C ***[1 mark]*** Boiling points increase down the group ***[1 mark]*** and xenon is further down the group than neon so will have the higher boiling point ***[1 mark]***.

Topic C2 — Bonding, Structure and Properties of Matter

Page 118 — Formation of Ions

1.1 Metal atoms usually lose electrons to become positive ions ***[1 mark]***.

1.2

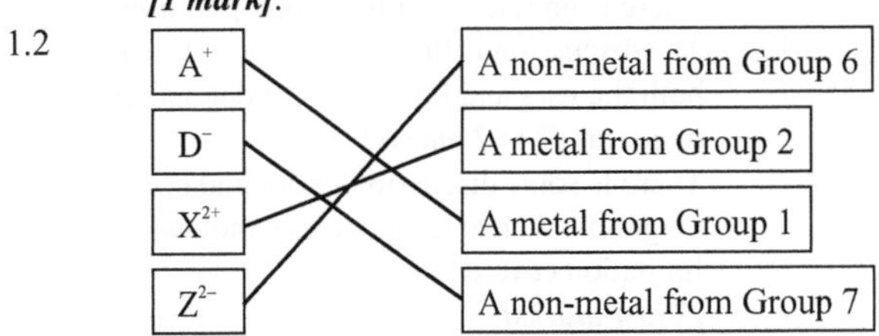

[2 marks if all four correct, otherwise 1 mark if two correct]

2.1 2– ***[1 mark]***

2.2 2,8,8 ***[1 mark]***. Sulfur gains two electrons ***[1 mark]*** to achieve a noble gas electronic structure/a full outer shell ***[1 mark]***.

2.3 Argon/Ar *[1 mark]*

Pages 119-120 — Ionic Bonding

Warm-up

Dot and cross diagram	Ionic formula
$[Na]^{+}$ $[Cl]^{-}$	NaCl
$[Na]^{+}$ $[O]^{2-}$ $[Na]^{+}$	Na_2O
$[Cl]^{-}$ $[Mg]^{2+}$ $[Cl]^{-}$	$MgCl_2$

1.1 calcium chloride *[1 mark]* and potassium oxide *[1 mark]*

Compounds that contain ionic bonding have to be made up of a metal and a non-metal. All the other options only contain non-metals, so can't be held together by ionic bonds.

1.2

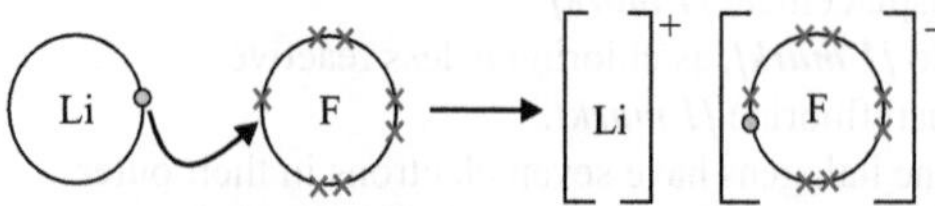

[1 mark for arrow showing electron transfer from Li to F, 1 mark for correct electronic structure of fluoride ion, with seven crosses and one dot, 1 mark for correct charges on the ions]

1.3 electrostatic attraction / electrostatic force *[1 mark]*

1.4 E.g. the particles in the compound are oppositely charged ions / have opposite charges / the bond is formed by electrons being transferred from one atom to another *[1 mark]*.

2.1 $[Mg]^{2+}$ ***[1 mark for no electrons in outer shell, 1 mark for correct charge]***

If you showed the second electron shell of magnesium containing eight electrons as dots, you also get the mark.

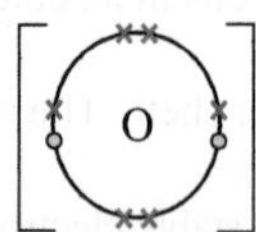

[1 mark for eight electrons in the outer shell, with two dots and six crosses, 1 mark for correct charge]

2.2 E.g. the magnesium atom transfers two electrons to the oxygen atom *[1 mark]*. A magnesium ion with a 2+ charge forms *[1 mark]*, and an oxide ion with a 2– charge forms *[1 mark]*. The oppositely charged ions are attracted to each other by electrostatic attraction *[1 mark]*.

3.1 Element X: Group 7 *[1 mark]*
Reason: Any one of, e.g. it has formed an ion by gaining 1 electron / it forms 1– ions / the uncharged element would have seven electrons in its outer shell *[1 mark]*.
Element Z: Group 2 *[1 mark]*
Reason: Any one of, e.g. it has formed an ion by losing 2 electrons / it forms 2+ ions / the uncharged element would have two electrons in its outer shell *[1 mark]*.

3.2 How to grade your answer:
Level 0: There is no relevant information *[No marks]*.
Level 1: The discussion is limited and doesn't mention both the uses and limitations of dot and cross diagrams *[1 to 2 marks]*.
Level 2: There is some discussion of dot and cross diagrams, with at least one use and one limitation covered *[3 to 4 marks]*.
Level 3: The discussion is comprehensive in evaluating both the uses and limitations of dot and cross diagrams *[5 to 6 marks]*.
Here are some points your answer may include:
<u>Dot and cross diagrams show:</u>
Charge of the ions.
The arrangement of electrons in an atom or ion.
Which atoms the electrons in an ion originally come from.
Empirical formula (correct ratio of ions).
<u>Dot and cross diagrams do not:</u>
Show the structure of the compound.
Correctly represent the sizes of ions.

Pages 121-122 — Ionic Compounds

Warm-up

In an ionic compound, the particles are held together by **strong** forces of attraction. These forces act **in all directions** which results in the particles bonding together to form **giant lattices**.

1.1 conduct electricity in the solid state *[1 mark]*

1.2 giant ionic lattice *[1 mark]*

2.1 Sodium chloride contains positive sodium ions (Na^+) *[1 mark]* and negative chloride ions (Cl^-) *[1 mark]* that are arranged in a regular lattice/giant ionic lattice *[1 mark]*. The oppositely charged ions are held together by electrostatic forces acting in all directions *[1 mark]*.

2.2 To melt sodium chloride, you have to overcome the very strong electrostatic forces/ionic bonds between the particles *[1 mark]*, which requires lots of energy *[1 mark]*.

3.1 E.g.

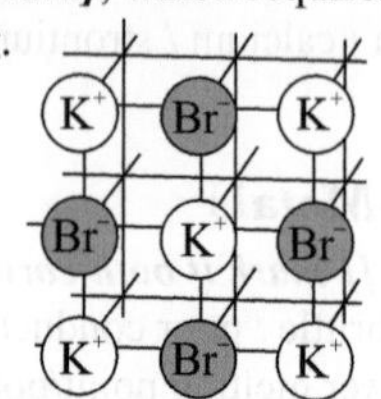

[1 mark for K^+ ions, 1 mark for Br^- ions, 1 mark for correct structure, with alternating ions]

You'd also get the marks if you labelled all the white circles as Br^- and all the grey circles as K^+.

3.2 Advantage: Any one of, e.g. the diagram shows the 3D arrangement of the ions / it suggests the structure is extended / it shows the regular (repeating) pattern of the ions *[1 mark]*.
Disadvantage: Any one of, e.g. the diagram doesn't correctly represent the sizes of ions / it shows gaps between the ions *[1 mark]*.

3.3 KBr *[1 mark]*

Remember that the overall charge of the ionic compound must be neutral. So you can work out the empirical formula by seeing that you only need one bromide ion to balance the charge on a potassium ion.

3.4 Boiling point: Potassium bromide has a giant structure with strong ionic bonds *[1 mark]*. In order to boil, these bonds need to be broken, which takes a lot of energy *[1 mark]*.
Electrical conductivity of solid: The ions are in fixed positions in the lattice *[1 mark]* and so are not able to move and carry a charge through the solid *[1 mark]*.
Electrical conductivity of solution: In solution, the ions are free to move *[1 mark]* and can carry a charge from place to place *[1 mark]*.

Pages 123-124 — Covalent Bonding

1.1 They share a pair of electrons *[1 mark]*.

1.2 Non-metals *[1 mark]*

1.3 BH_3 *[1 mark]*

Find the molecular formula by counting up how many atoms of each element there are in the diagram.

2

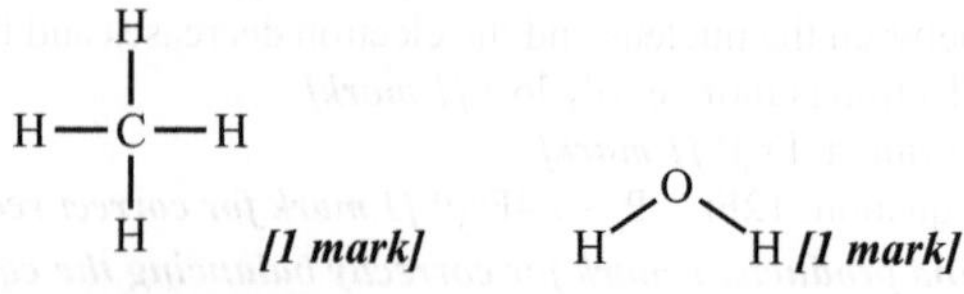

O=O *[1 mark]*

Each line represents one covalent bond. Oxygen has a double bond, so you need to draw two lines between the oxygen atoms to show this.

3.1 E.g. it contains only non-metals *[1 mark]* and Figure 1 shows shared electrons *[1 mark]*.

3.2 Any two from, e.g. they don't show how the atoms are arranged in space / they don't show the relative sizes of the atoms. ***[2 marks — 1 mark for each correct answer]***

3.3 One electron from hydrogen and one from carbon form a shared pair ***[1 mark]*** that are attracted to the nuclei of the carbon and hydrogen atoms ***[1 mark]*** by electrostatic attraction ***[1 mark]***.

4.1 Displayed formula: e.g. it shows how all the atoms in a molecule are connected in a simple way ***[1 mark]***, but it doesn't show the 3D structure of the molecule / it doesn't show which atom the electrons in the bond originally come from ***[1 mark]***.
Dot and cross diagram: e.g. it shows where the electrons in each covalent bond originally came from ***[1 mark]*** but it doesn't show the 3D structure of the molecule / they can become very complicated if the molecule is large ***[1 mark]***.
3D model: e.g. it shows how all the atoms are arranged in space in relation to each other / it shows the correct bond angles in the molecule ***[1 mark]*** but it quickly becomes complicated for large molecules / you can't tell which atom in the bonds the electrons originally came from ***[1 mark]***.

4.2 The displayed formula ***[1 mark]*** would be the best as it is easy to see how the atoms in a large molecule are connected without the diagram becoming too complicated ***[1 mark]***.

Pages 125-126 — Simple Molecular Substances

1.1 The bonds between the atoms are strong ***[1 mark]***, but the forces between the molecules are weak ***[1 mark]***.

1.2 The weak forces between the molecules / the intermolecular forces ***[1 mark]***.

2.1

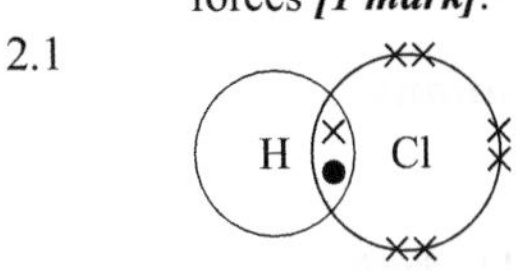

[1 mark for correct number of electrons, 1 mark for one shared pair]

2.2

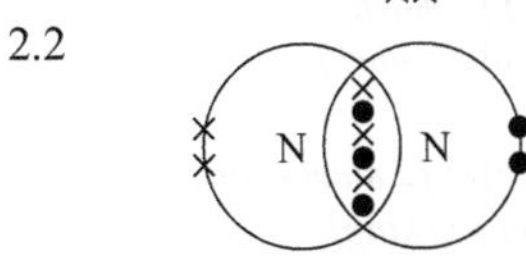

[1 mark for correct number of electrons, 1 mark for three shared pairs]

2.3 E.g. N_2 has a triple covalent bond, whilst HCl has a single covalent bond ***[1 mark]***.

3.1 Simple molecular substances have weak forces between molecules ***[1 mark]*** so not much energy is needed to overcome them/they normally have low melting points ***[1 mark]***.

3.2 Iodine won't conduct electricity ***[1 mark]*** because the I_2 molecules aren't charged / the electrons aren't free to move so can't carry a charge ***[1 mark]***.

4.1 When methane boils, the forces between the molecules are overcome ***[1 mark]*** and it turns from a liquid into a gas ***[1 mark]***. Methane is a smaller molecule then butane ***[1 mark]*** so the forces between the molecules are weaker ***[1 mark]*** and less energy is needed to overcome them ***[1 mark]***.

4.2 Carbon needs four more electrons to get a full outer shell, and does this by forming four covalent bonds ***[1 mark]***. Hydrogen only needs one more electron to complete its outer shell, so can only form one covalent bond ***[1 mark]***.

Remember that the outer electron shell in hydrogen only needs two electrons to be filled, not eight like other electron shells.

4.3 Four ***[1 mark]***. Silicon has four outer electrons so needs four more to get a full outer shell / silicon has the same number of outer shell electrons as carbon so will form the same number of bonds ***[1 mark]***.

Page 127 — Polymers and Giant Covalent Substances

Warm-up

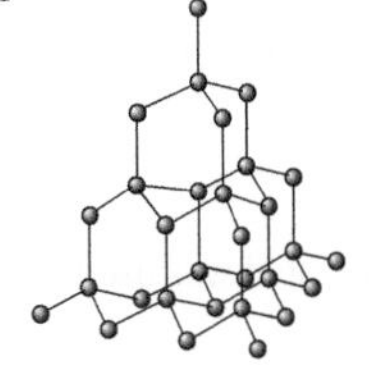

1.1 Ammonia ***[1 mark]***

Ammonia has a simple covalent structure — it forms small molecules.

1.2 The covalent bonds are very strong ***[1 mark]***, so a lot of energy is needed to break them ***[1 mark]***.

2.1 $(C_2H_4)_n$ ***[1 mark]***

2.2 Solid ***[1 mark]***. The molecule is very large and so the intermolecular forces are strong ***[1 mark]*** and need lots of energy to be broken ***[1 mark]***.

2.3 covalent bonds ***[1 mark]***

Page 128 — Allotropes of Carbon

1.1

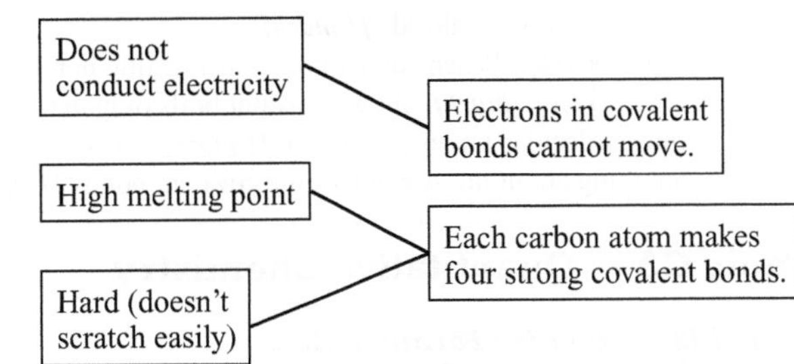

[2 marks if all three correct, otherwise 1 mark if one correct]

1.2 A: graphene ***[1 mark]***
B: buckminster fullerene ***[1 mark]***
C: carbon nanotube / fullerene ***[1 mark]***

1.3 Any one of, e.g. to strengthen materials / to deliver drugs into the body / as a catalyst / as a lubricant / in electronics ***[1 mark]***

2.1 Graphite is made up of sheets of carbon atoms arranged in hexagons ***[1 mark]***, with weak forces between the sheets ***[1 mark]***. Each carbon atom forms three covalent bonds ***[1 mark]***, and has one delocalised electron ***[1 mark]***.

2.2 Graphite has delocalised electrons ***[1 mark]*** which are free to move through the substance and carry an electric charge ***[1 mark]***.

Page 129 — Metallic Bonding

1.1 E.g.

Metal ions in a regular pattern

Delocalised electrons

[1 mark for regular arrangement of metal ions, 1 mark for delocalised electron, 1 mark for correct labels]

1.2 There is a strong electrostatic attraction ***[1 mark]*** between the delocalised electrons and the positive metal ions ***[1 mark]***.

1.3 High ***[1 mark]*** because the bonding is strong so requires lots of energy to break ***[1 mark]***.

1.4 Good ***[1 mark]*** because the electrons are free to move throughout the structure and carry an electrical charge ***[1 mark]***.

2.1 Metallic structures have layers of atoms ***[1 mark]*** that are able to slide over one another ***[1 mark]***.

2.2 Atoms of different elements are different sizes ***[1 mark]***. Adding atoms of a different size to a pure metal distorts the layers
[1 mark] making it harder for them to slide over one another ***[1 mark]***.

Page 130 — States of Matter

1.1 solid, liquid, gas ***[1 mark]***

1.2 $NaCl_{(s)}$: solid ***[1 mark]***
$O_{2(g)}$: gas ***[1 mark]***
$Hg_{(l)}$: liquid ***[1 mark]***

2.1 solid spheres ***[1 mark]***

2.2 liquid ***[1 mark]***

2.3 Any two from: melting / boiling / condensing / freezing ***[1 mark for each]***

2.4 Any two from: e.g. the model says nothing about forces

between particles / particles aren't really spheres / particles are mostly empty space, not solid ***[1 mark for each]***.

Page 131 — Changing State

1.1 melting ***[1 mark]***
1.2 boiling point ***[1 mark]***
1.3 The bonds are strong ***[1 mark]***.
2.1 sodium chloride ***[1 mark]***
At 900 °C, water would be a gas and copper would be a solid.
2.2 Sodium chloride ***[1 mark]*** and water ***[1 mark]***.
At 1500 °C, copper would be a liquid.
2.3 Boiling sodium chloride ***[1 mark]***.
2.4 No ***[1 mark]***. When copper boils, the metallic bonds are broken ***[1 mark]***, but when water boils only the intermolecular forces are broken ***[1 mark]***, so you can't tell anything about the strength of the covalent bonds ***[1 mark]***.

Topic C3 — Quantitative Chemistry

Page 132 — Relative Formula Mass

1
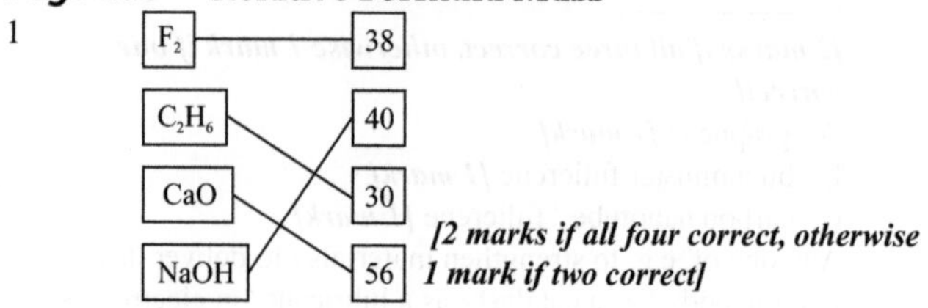

[2 marks if all four correct, otherwise 1 mark if two correct]

2.1 $M_r(MgO) = 24 + 16 = 40$ ***[1 mark]***
percentage by mass of magnesium $= \frac{A_r(Mg)}{M_r(MgO)} \times 100$
$= \frac{24}{40} \times 100 =$ **60%** ***[1 mark]***
2.2 Mass of magnesium ions $= 200 \times \frac{15}{100} =$ **30 g** ***[1 mark]***
2.3 Mass of magnesium oxide containing 30 g of magnesium ions $= 30 \div (60 \div 100) =$ **50 g** ***[1 mark]***
If you used the percentage mass of magnesium ions as 40% and the mass of magnesium ions in the mixture as 20 g, your answer will also be 50 g.

Page 133 — The Mole

Warm-up
6.02×10^{23}
1.1 M_r of carbon dioxide $= 12 + (16 \times 2) =$ **44** ***[1 mark]***
1.2 Moles of carbon dioxide $= 110 \div 44 =$ **2.5 mol** ***[1 mark]***
1.3 1 mole of carbon dioxide would weigh more ***[1 mark]***. It has a higher relative formula mass ***[1 mark]***.
2.1 2 mol sulfur $= 2 \times 32$ g $=$ **64 g** ***[1 mark]***
2.2 M_r of iron sulfide $= 56 + 32 = 88$
Moles of iron sulfide $= 44 \div 88 =$ **0.50 mol** ***[2 marks for correct answer, otherwise 1 mark for correct working]***
2.3 The number of atoms in 3 moles of sulfur is greater than the number of molecules in 2 moles of iron sulfide ***[1 mark]***. There's the same number of atoms in 1 mole of sulfur as there are molecules in 1 mole of iron sulfide so in 3 moles of sulfur there will be more atoms than there are molecules in 2 moles of iron sulfide ***[1 mark]***.

Pages 134-136 — Conservation of Mass

1.1 $2Mg + O_2 \rightarrow 2MgO$ ***[1 mark]***
1.2 Mass of oxygen = 20 g of MgO – 12 g of Mg = **8 g** ***[2 marks for correct answer, otherwise 1 mark for correct working]***
2.1 The mass of reactants equals the mass of products in a chemical reaction ***[1 mark]***. Atoms are not made or destroyed during a chemical reaction ***[1 mark]***. So, there must be the same number of each type of atom in the products as in the reactants ***[1 mark]***.
2.2 The mass of the powder would increase ***[1 mark]***. Oxygen gas was not included as part of the original measurement ***[1 mark]***. Particles of oxygen are added to the zinc to form zinc oxide powder ***[1 mark]***.
3.1 The measurement is correct ***[1 mark]***. Carbon dioxide (a gas) is produced and released into the atmosphere ***[1 mark]***. So, the student only measured the mass of the solid product, not both products ***[1 mark]***.
3.2 M_r of sodium oxide $= 106 - 44 =$ **62** ***[1 mark]***
3.3 Moles of $Na_2CO_3 = 53 \div 106 = 0.50$
For every mole of Na_2CO_3 that reacts, 1 mole of CO_2 is produced. Only 0.50 moles of Na_2CO_3 react so 0.50 moles of CO_2 are produced.
Mass of carbon dioxide $= 0.50 \times 44 =$ **22 g** ***[3 marks for correct answer, otherwise 1 mark for 0.50 moles of Na_2CO_3 and 1 mark for a 1:1 molar ratio]***
To work out a molar ratio, you need to use the balanced symbol equation for the reaction. The numbers in front of the chemical formulas show the number of moles of a substance that react or are produced in the reaction. In this question, for every 1 mole Na_2CO_3 heated, 1 mole of carbon dioxide is produced — a 1:1 molar ratio.
3.4 Mass of sodium oxide = 53 g – 22 g = **31 g** ***[1 mark]***
4.1 E.g. the reading of the final mass might have been taken before the reaction completed ***[1 mark]***.
4.2 Table 1: Range $= 1.42 - 1.31 = 0.11$ g
uncertainty = range $\div 2 = 0.11 \div 2 = \pm 0.055$ g ***[1 mark]***
percentage uncertainty $= (0.055 \div 1.37) \times 100\%$
$= 4.0\%$ (to 2 s.f.) ***[1 mark]***
Table 2: Range $= 2.75 - 2.66 = 0.09$ g
uncertainty = range $\div 2 = 0.09 \div 2 = \pm 0.045$ g ***[1 mark]***
percentage uncertainty $= (0.045 \div 2.71) \times 100\%$
$= 1.7\%$ (to 2 s.f.) ***[1 mark]***
4.3 The size of the uncertainty is similar in both sets of results, but the percentage uncertainty is greater in table 1 ***[1 mark]***. This suggests that the size of the random errors in the measurement of the final mass was similar in both sets of experiments ***[1 mark]***, but the effect of these errors is smaller in table 2 because the experiments in table 2 used a larger initial mass of the compound ***[1 mark]***.

Pages 137-138 — The Mole and Equations

Warm-up
3
1 $H_2SO_4 + 2NaOH \rightarrow Na_2SO_4 + 2H_2O$ ***[1 mark]***
2.1 Moles of sodium $= 9.2 \div 23 =$ **0.4 mol** ***[1 mark]***
2.2 M_r of water $= (1 \times 2) + 16 = 18$
Moles of water $= 7.2$ g $\div 18 =$ **0.4 mol** ***[2 marks for correct answer, otherwise 1 mark for correct working]***
2.3 Divide the number of moles of each substance by the lowest of these number of moles (0.2 mol) to give the molar ratios.
Na $= 0.4 \div 0.2 = 2$ mol
$H_2O = 0.4 \div 0.2 = 2$ mol
NaOH $= 0.4 \div 0.2 = 2$ mol
$H_2 = 0.2 \div 0.2 = 1$ mol
$\mathbf{2Na + 2H_2O \rightarrow 2NaOH + H_2}$ ***[3 marks for correct answer, otherwise 1 mark for correct method and 1 mark for at least 2 correct numbers in the equation]***
3.1 Moles of methane = 8 g ÷ 16 = 0.5 mol
Moles of oxygen = 32 g ÷ 32 = 1 mol
Moles of carbon dioxide = 22 g ÷ 44 = 0.5 mol
Moles of water = 18 g ÷ 18 = 1 mol ***[1 mark]***
Divide by the lowest of these numbers which is 0.5:
Methane = 0.5 ÷ 0.5 = 1 mol
Oxygen = 1 ÷ 0.5 = 2 mol
Carbon dioxide = 0.5 ÷ 0.5 = 1 mol
Water = 1 ÷ 0.5 = 2 mol ***[1 mark]***
$\mathbf{CH_4 + 2O_2 \rightarrow CO_2 + 2H_2O}$ ***[1 mark]***
3.2 Moles of oxygen = 48 g ÷ 32 = 1.5 mol
Molar ratio of oxygen : carbon dioxide = 2:1
Moles of carbon dioxide = 1.5 mol ÷ 2 = **0.75 mol** ***[3 marks for correct answer, otherwise 1 mark for 1.5 mol of oxygen and 1 mark for molar ratio of 2:1]***
3.3 Molar ratio of $CH_4 : H_2O = 1:2$
4 mol of methane will produce **8 mol** of water ***[1 mark]***.
3.4 Mass of water $= 18 \times 8 =$ **144 g** ***[1 mark]***
If you got the equation wrong in 3.1 but used all the right working in parts 3.2, 3.3 and 3.4, you still get the marks, even if you got a different answer to the one here.

Page 139 — Limiting Reactants

1.1 To make sure that all the hydrochloric acid was used up in the reaction ***[1 mark]***.

1.2 The limiting reactant is completely used up during a reaction *[1 mark]* and so its quantity limits the amount of product that can be formed *[1 mark]*.

2.1 Molar ratio of copper oxide : copper sulfate = 1:1
Therefore, 0.50 mol of copper sulfate is produced.
M_r of copper sulfate = 63.5 + 32 + (16 × 4) = 159.5
Mass of copper sulfate = 0.50 × 159.5 = **80 g** ***[3 marks for correct answer, otherwise 1 mark for 0.50 moles of copper sulfate and 1 mark for M_r of 159.5]***

2.2 The amount of product formed is directly proportional to the amount of limiting reactant *[1 mark]*. So doubling the quantity of the sulfuric acid will double the mass of the copper sulfate *[1 mark]*.

2.3 If only 0.4 mol of copper oxide is present, there will not be enough molecules to react with all the sulfuric acid *[1 mark]*. The copper oxide will be the limiting reactant *[1 mark]* and only 0.4 mol of product will be formed *[1 mark]*.

Page 140 — Concentrations of Solutions

1.1 Conc. of calcium chloride = 28 g ÷ 0.4 dm³ = **70 g/dm³** *[1 mark for correct answer and 1 mark for correct units]*

1.2 The concentration of a solution is the amount of a substance in a given volume of a solution *[1 mark]*.

2.1 Volume in dm³ = 500 ÷ 1000 = 0.50 dm³ *[1 mark]*.
Concentration = 40.0 ÷ 0.500 = **80** g/dm³ *[1 mark]*.

2.2 Mass = 60.0 × 0.500 = **30** g *[1 mark]*.

2.3 Mean = (18.2 + 18.1 + 18.4 + 18.5) ÷ 4 = **18.3 g/dm³** *[1 mark]*

2.4 Range = 18.5 – 18.1 = 0.4
Uncertainty = range ÷ 2 = 0.4 ÷ 2 = **± 0.2 g/dm³** *[2 marks for correct answer, otherwise 1 mark for calculating range]*

Topic C4 — Chemical Changes

Page 141 — Acids and Bases

Warm-up

Universal indicator will turn **red** in strongly acidic solutions and **purple** in strongly alkaline solutions. In a **neutral** solution, Universal indicator will be green. A pH probe attached to a pH meter is **more** accurate than Universal indicator as it displays a numerical value for pH.

1.1 beer *[1 mark]*

1.2 blue / blue-green *[1 mark]*

1.3 H^+ *[1 mark]*

1.4 0 *[1 mark]* – 14 *[1 mark]*

2.1 acid + alkali → salt + water *[1 mark]*

2.2 $H^+_{(aq)} + OH^-_{(aq)} \rightarrow H_2O_{(l)}$ *[1 mark]*

You still get the marks if you didn't include state symbols.

Page 142 — Strong Acids and Weak Acids

1.1 A strong acid completely ionises/dissociates in solution *[1 mark]*. A weak acid only partly ionises in solution *[1 mark]*.

1.2 Nitric acid would have a lower pH than ethanoic acid *[1 mark]* because it is a stronger acid/more dissociated/ionised *[1 mark]*, so the concentration of H^+ would be greater *[1 mark]*.

You would also get the marks for using the reverse argument — ethanoic acid would have a higher pH because it is a weaker acid so the concentration of H^+ ions is lower.

1.3 3 *[1 mark]*

As the concentration of H^+ ions in solution decreases by a factor of 10, the pH rises by 1.

1.4 Adding water to the beaker *[1 mark]*.
Adding ethanoic acid to the beaker at the same concentration as the citric acid *[1 mark]*.
Changing the citric acid to carbonic acid of the same concentration *[1 mark]*.

Pages 143-144 — Reactions of Acids

1.1 Neutralisation *[1 mark]*

1.2 Fizzing — Carbon dioxide is produced *[1 mark]*

2.1 sulfuric acid + lithium hydroxide → lithium sulfate + water *[1 mark]*

2.2 $H_2SO_4 + 2LiOH \rightarrow Li_2SO_4 + 2H_2O$ ***[1 mark for correct formula of Li_2SO_4, 1 mark for correct balancing]***

2.3 Both reactions produce lithium sulfate and water *[1 mark]*. The reaction between sulfuric acid and lithium carbonate also produces carbon dioxide *[1 mark]*.

3.1 Add zinc oxide to hydrochloric acid until the reaction stops / the excess metal oxide sinks to the bottom *[1 mark]*. Filter the excess solid from the solution using a filter funnel *[1 mark]*. Heat the zinc chloride solution to evaporate some of the water and then leave to cool *[1 mark]*. Filter and dry the crystals that form *[1 mark]*.

3.2 E.g. zinc carbonate *[1 mark]*.

Any other insoluble zinc base or zinc metal also gets a mark.

4 How to grade your answer:

Level 0: Nothing written worth of credit *[No marks]*.

Level 1: Some suitable tests are named but it is not clear how the results would enable the solutions to be identified. The chemistry of the tests is not clearly described *[1 to 2 marks]*.

Level 2: Tests that enable at least one solution to be identified are clearly described, or tests that would enable all solutions to be identified are named but not clearly described *[3 to 4 marks]*.

Level 3: At least two tests are described together with the expected outcomes. It is clear how these tests would be used to distinguish between all three solutions. The chemistry of the tests is correctly described *[5 to 6 marks]*.

Here are some points your answer may include:
Test the pH of each solution.
The neutral solution/the solution that turns Universal indicator green is the salt.
Add a couple of drops of Universal indicator to the solutions followed by some dilute acid.
The solution containing sodium carbonate will fizz as it reacts with the acid to release carbon dioxide gas as shown by the equation: acid + sodium carbonate → sodium salt + water + carbon dioxide
The solution containing sodium hydroxide will react with acid changing the Universal indicator solution from blue/purple to green, but there won't be any fizzing as no gas is released as shown by the reaction:
acid + sodium hydroxide → sodium salt + water
The solution containing the sodium salt won't react with acid.

Pages 145-146 — The Reactivity Series

1.1 magnesium + hydrochloric acid → magnesium chloride + hydrogen *[1 mark]*

1.2 Positive magnesium ions *[1 mark]*

1.3 It forms positive ions less easily / it's lower down in the reactivity series *[1 mark]*.

1.4 Any one of: e.g. potassium / sodium / lithium / calcium *[1 mark]*.

2.1 metal + water → metal hydroxide + hydrogen *[1 mark]*

2.2 $Ca_{(s)} + 2H_2O_{(l)} \rightarrow Ca(OH)_{2(aq)} + H_{2(g)}$ ***[1 mark for each correct product]***

2.3 Any one from: e.g. lithium / sodium / potassium *[1 mark]* As it is higher in the reactivity series than calcium / loses electrons more easily than calcium / forms positive ions more easily *[1 mark]*.

2.4 potassium, sodium, zinc *[1 mark]*

3.1 When a metal reacts with an acid, the metal forms positive ions *[1 mark]*. The results show that lithium reacts more vigorously with acid than magnesium does *[1 mark]*, so lithium forms positive ions more easily *[1 mark]*.

3.2 A very vigorous fizzing/more vigorous than lithium *[1 mark]*, sodium disappears *[1 mark]*.

3.3 lithium, calcium, copper *[1 mark]*

3.4 It is not possible to tell the difference between magnesium and zinc from these results since both have same reaction with dilute acid *[1 mark]*. E.g. to find which is more reactive, you could find the effect of adding zinc to water *[1 mark]*.

Page 147 — Separating Metals from Metal Oxides

1.1 E.g. gold *[1 mark]*

1.2 Many metals can react with other elements/oxygen to form compounds/oxides *[1 mark]*.

1.3 Reduction is the loss of oxygen *[1 mark]*.

1.4 Magnesium is more reactive than carbon ***[1 mark]***.

2.1 $2Fe_2O_3 + 3C \rightarrow 4Fe + 3CO_2$
[1 mark for correct equation, 1 mark for correct balancing]

2.2 Carbon has been oxidised ***[1 mark]*** as it has gained oxygen during this reaction ***[1 mark]***.

2.3 E.g. extracting magnesium would have high energy costs to provide the high temperature and reduced pressure needed ***[1 mark]***, but iron extraction doesn't need to be continuously heated ***[1 mark]***.

Page 148 — Redox Reactions

1.1 Reduction is the gain of electrons ***[1 mark]***.

1.2 zinc chloride + sodium → zinc + sodium chloride ***[1 mark]***

1.3 Hydrogen gains electrons ***[1 mark]***.

1.4 Chlorine is neither oxidised nor reduced ***[1 mark]***.

2.1 $Mg_{(s)} + Fe^{2+}_{(aq)} \rightarrow Mg^{2+}_{(aq)} + Fe_{(s)}$ ***[1 mark]***

You still get the marks if you didn't include state symbols.

2.2 No reaction would occur ***[1 mark]***. Copper is less reactive than iron so doesn't displace it ***[1 mark]***.

Pages 149-151 — Electrolysis

Warm-up

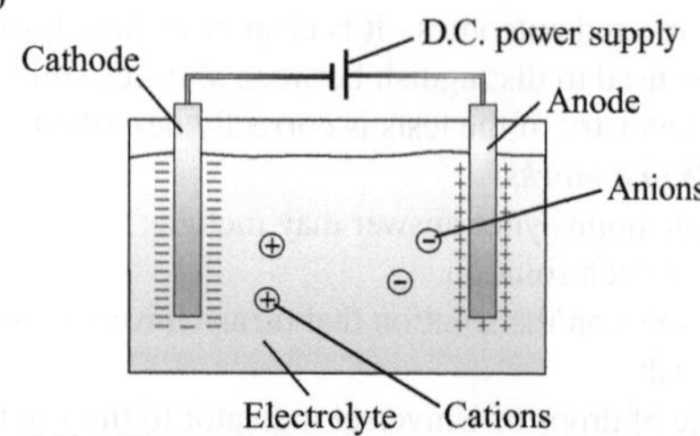

1.1 A liquid or solution that can conduct electricity ***[1 mark]***.

1.2 lead bromide → lead + bromine ***[1 mark]***

1.3 Lead ions have a positive charge ***[1 mark]***. This means they are attracted to the negative cathode ***[1 mark]***.

1.4 Br^- ***[1 mark]***

1.5 oxidation ***[1 mark]***

1.6 So the ions can move to the electrodes ***[1 mark]***.

2.1 molten aluminium ***[1 mark]***

2.2 To lower the melting point of the electrolyte ***[1 mark]***.

2.3 Carbon in the electrodes reacts with oxygen to form carbon dioxide ***[1 mark]***, so they degrade over time ***[1 mark]***.

3.1 Iron ions, chloride ions, hydrogen ions and hydroxide ions
[1 mark for iron ions and chloride ions, 1 mark for hydrogen ions and hydroxide ions].

3.2 At the cathode: hydrogen is discharged.
At the anode: chlorine is discharged ***[1 mark]***.

3.3 oxygen ***[1 mark]***

3.4 Iron can be extracted via reduction with carbon ***[1 mark]***, which is less expensive than electrolysis ***[1 mark]***.

4.1 E.g.

D.C. power supply
Boiling tubes filled with solution to capture any gas produced
Inert anode / positive electrode
Inert cathode / negative electrode
Aqueous solution / electrolyte

[1 mark for power supply, 1 mark for electrodes in solution, 1 mark for boiling tubes over the electrodes, 1 mark for labels]

4.2

Solution	Product at cathode	Product at anode
$CuCl_2$	Cu	Cl_2
KBr	H_2	Br_2
H_2SO_4	H_2	O_2 and H_2O

[1 mark for each correct answer]

4.3 Potassium is more reactive than hydrogen ***[1 mark]*** so hydrogen is discharged ***[1 mark]***. There are no halide ions ***[1 mark]*** so oxygen and water are discharged ***[1 mark]***.

4.4 Cathode: $2H^+ + 2e^- \rightarrow H_2$ ***[1 mark]***
Anode: $4OH^- \rightarrow O_2 + 2H_2O + 4e^-$
/ $4OH^- - 4e^- \rightarrow O_2 + 2H_2O$ ***[1 mark]***

Topic C5 — Energy Changes

Pages 152-154 — Exothermic and Endothermic Reactions

1 In an endothermic reaction, energy is transferred from the surroundings so the temperature of the surroundings goes down ***[1 mark]***.

2.1 endothermic ***[1 mark]***

2.2

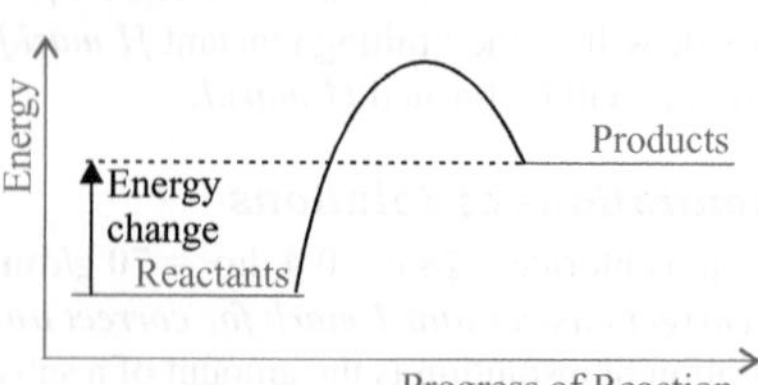

[1 mark for correct curve, 1 mark for energy change]

The curve has to go above the energy of the products and then fall back down. If you didn't do this, you don't get the mark.

2.3 From the surroundings ***[1 mark]***.

2.4 It stays the same ***[1 mark]***.

2.5 E.g. a sports injury pack ***[1 mark]***.

3.1 The activation energy is the minimum amount of energy that reactants must have when they collide with each other in order to react ***[1 mark]***. It's shown by the difference between the energy of the reactants and the maximum energy reached by the curve on the reaction profile ***[1 mark]***.

3.2 Reaction A is the most suitable reaction ***[1 mark]***.
Reaction C is endothermic, so would not give out heat, and couldn't be used to warm your hands ***[1 mark]***.
Reaction A has a lower activation energy than Reaction B / gives out more energy than Reaction B ***[1 mark]***.

4.1 Any three from: e.g. thermometer / polystyrene cup (and lid) / mass balance / measuring cylinder / beaker filled with cotton wool / stopwatch ***[1 mark for each]***.

4.2 How to grade your answer:

Level 0: There is no relevant information ***[No marks]***.

Level 1: The method is vague, and misses out important details about how the investigation could be carried out ***[1 to 2 marks]***.

Level 2: The method is clear, but misses out a few key details about how the investigation would be carried out or how the variables could be controlled
[3 to 4 marks].

Level 3: There is a clear and detailed method that includes ways to reduce energy transfer to the surroundings, and specifies variables that should be controlled throughout the investigation
[5 to 6 marks].

Here are some points your answer may include:
Measure out an exact volume of the acid solution into the polystyrene cup.
Record the initial temperature of the acid solution.
Add one metal powder and stir the mixture.
Place a lid on the polystyrene cup to reduce the amount of energy transferred to the surroundings.
Take the temperature of the mixture every 30 seconds and record the highest temperature.
Repeat the experiment for each different metal.
Use the same volume and concentration of acid each time you repeat the experiment.
Make sure the acid starts at the same temperature each time you repeat the experiment.
Use the same number of moles and the same surface area of metal each time you repeat the experiment.

5.1 E.g.

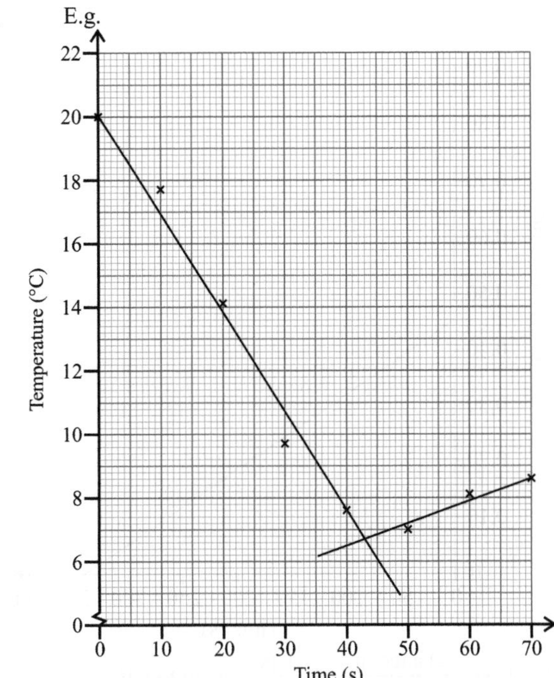

[2 marks for all points plotted correctly, otherwise 1 mark for at least six points plotted correctly. 1 mark for two sensible lines of best fit.]

5.2 Intersection of lines of best fit = 6.7 °C (allow between 6.2 and 7.2 °C)
Maximum temperature change = 20.0 – 6.7 = **13.3 °C** (allow between 12.8 and 13.8 °C)
[2 marks for the correct answer, otherwise 1 mark for finding the temperature at the intersection]

Page 155 — Bond Energies

1.1 Energy to break the bonds = (4 × C–H) + Cl–Cl
= (4 × 413) + 243 = 1652 + 243 = 1895 kJ/mol
Energy produced when bonds form = (3 × C–H) + C–Cl + H–Cl
= (3 × 413) + 346 + 432 = 1239 + 346 + 432
= 2017 kJ/mol
Energy change of reaction = Energy to break bonds – Energy produced when bonds form
= 1895 – 2017 = **–122 kJ/mol** ***[3 marks for correct answer, otherwise 1 mark for 1895 kJ/mol, 1 mark for 2017 kJ/mol, 1 mark for subtracting energy produced when bonds form from energy needed to break bonds]***

Three of the C–H bonds are unchanged in this reaction. So you could also calculate this by working out just the energy needed to break the C–H and the Cl–Cl bond, and subtracting the energy that's released when the new C–Cl and H–Cl bonds form.

1.2 The reaction is exothermic ***[1 mark]*** because the energy released when the bonds of the products form is greater than the energy needed to break the bonds of the reactants ***[1 mark]***.

2 Total energy needed to break the bonds in the reactants
= H–H + F–F = 436 + 158 = 594 kJ/mol
Energy change of reaction = Energy needed to break bonds – Energy released when bonds form
So, energy released when bonds form = Energy needed to break bonds – Energy change of reaction
= 594 – (–542) = 1136 kJ/mol
Energy released when bonds form = 2 × H–F bond energy
So, H–F bond energy = 1136 ÷ 2 = **568 kJ/mol**
[3 marks for correct answer, otherwise 1 mark for finding the energy needed to break the bonds, 1 mark for finding the energy released by forming bonds]

Topic C6 — The Rate and Extent of Chemical Change

Pages 156-158 — Rates of Reaction

1.1 Using a larger volume of the solution, but keeping the concentration the same ***[1 mark]***.

1.2 activation energy ***[1 mark]***

1.3 A catalyst decreases the activation energy ***[1 mark]***.

2 Produced most product: C ***[1 mark]***
Finished first: B ***[1 mark]***
Started at the slowest rate: A ***[1 mark]***

3.1

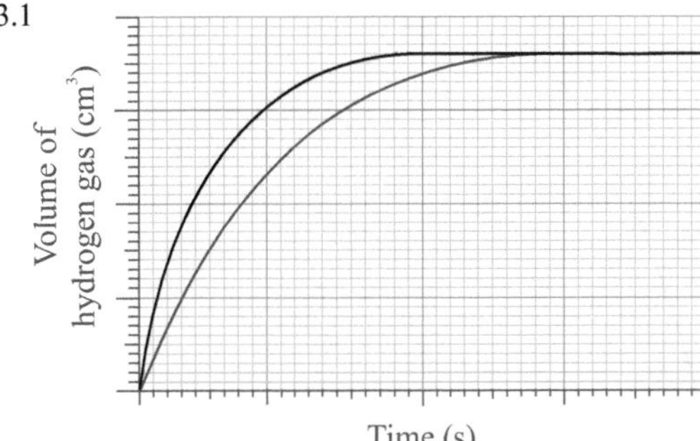

[1 mark for curve with steeper gradient at the start of the reaction, 1 mark for curve reaching the final volume earlier, 1 mark for final volume being the same as for the other curve]

3.2 The frequency of the collisions ***[1 mark]*** and the energy of the colliding particles ***[1 mark]***.

3.3 There are more particles in a given volume/the particles are closer together ***[1 mark]***, so the collisions between particles are more frequent ***[1 mark]***.

3.4 The rate would increase ***[1 mark]***.

3.5 Smaller pieces have a higher surface area to volume ratio ***[1 mark]***. So for the same volume of solid, the particles around it will have more area to work on and collisions will be more frequent ***[1 mark]***.

3.6 E.g. changing the temperature / adding a catalyst ***[1 mark]***.

4.1 E.g. increasing the volume of the reaction vessel would decrease the pressure of the reacting gases ***[1 mark]***. So the particles would be more spread out and would collide less frequently ***[1 mark]***, so the reaction rate would decrease ***[1 mark]***.
Increasing the temperature would cause the particles to move faster, so the frequency of collisions would increase ***[1 mark]*** and the reaction rate would increase ***[1 mark]***.

4.2 It's a catalyst ***[1 mark]***.

4.3 The reaction equation won't change ***[1 mark]***. Cerium oxide isn't used up in the reaction, so doesn't appear in the reaction equation ***[1 mark]***.

4.4

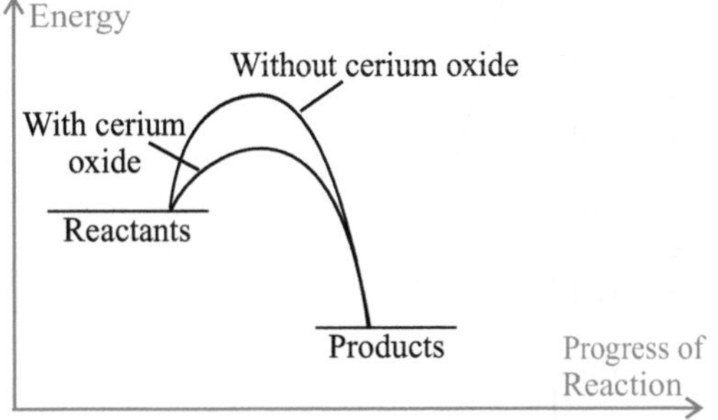

[1 mark for correct relative energies of products and reactants, 1 mark for start and end energies being the same for reactions with and without cerium oxide, 1 mark for reaction with cerium oxide rising to a lower energy than reaction without cerium oxide]

Pages 159-161 — Measuring Rates of Reaction

Warm-up

The rate of a reaction can be measured by dividing the amount of **reactants** used up or the amount of **products** formed by the **time**. To find the rate at a particular time from a graph with a curved line of best fit, you have to find the **gradient** of the **tangent** at that time.

1 mass ***[1 mark]***, volume of gas ***[1 mark]***

2.1 time taken for the solution to go cloudy ***[1 mark]***

2.2 temperature ***[1 mark]***

2.3 Any one from: e.g. the concentration of the reactants / the volume of the reactants / the depth of the reaction mixture ***[1 mark]***.

2.4 It would be more accurate to measure the volume of gas produced ***[1 mark]*** as this method less subjective ***[1 mark]***.

3.1 E.g. a gas syringe / a measuring cylinder inverted in a bowl of water ***[1 mark]***.

3.2

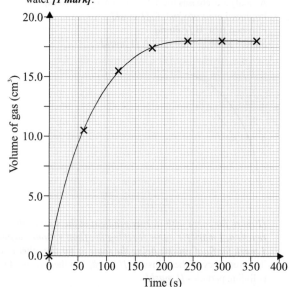

[2 marks for all points plotted correctly, or 1 mark for at least 5 points plotted correctly, 1 mark for line of best fit]

3.3 Any value between 210-240 s ***[1 mark]***

When no more gas is produced, the reaction has stopped.

3.4 E.g. Mean rate of reaction = $\frac{\text{amount of product formed}}{\text{time for reaction to stop}}$

$= \frac{18.0}{240} = \mathbf{0.075\ cm^3/s}$

[2 marks for correct answer between 0.075-0.086 cm³/s, otherwise 1 mark for correct equation]

If you got the wrong answer in 3.3, but used it correctly here as the change in y, you still get all the marks.

3.5 E.g. repeat the experiment using the same method ***[1 mark]*** and check that the results are similar ***[1 mark]***.

4.1

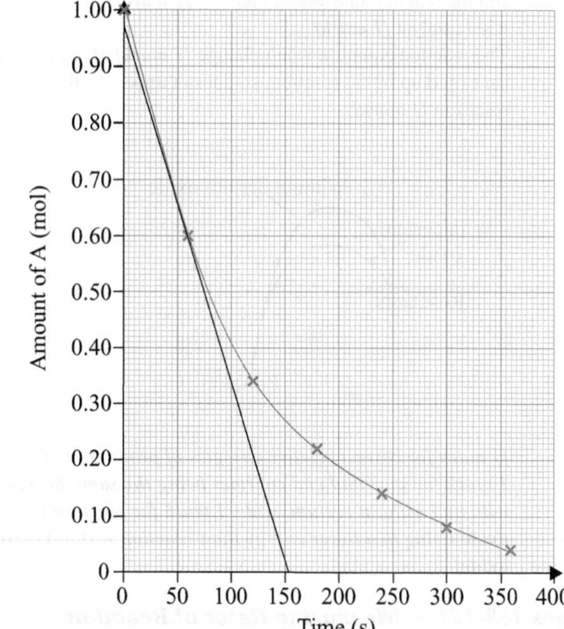

Gradient = $\frac{\text{change in } y}{\text{change in } x} = \frac{0.97}{153} = \mathbf{0.0063\ mol/s}$

(allow between 0.0053 mol/s and 0.0073 mol/s)

[4 marks for correct answer, otherwise 1 mark for correctly drawn tangent to curve at 50 s, 1 mark for answer to 2 s.f., 1 mark for correct units]

4.2

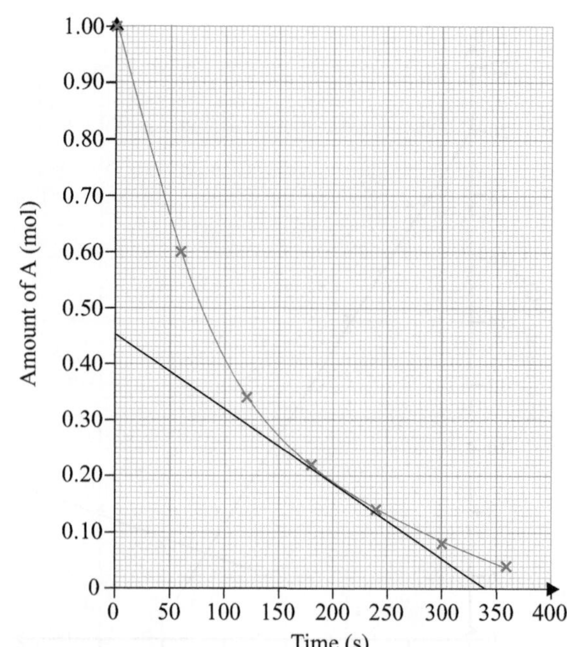

Gradient = $\frac{\text{change in } y}{\text{change in } x} = \frac{0.45}{340} = \mathbf{0.0013\ mol/s}$

(allow between 0.0008 mol/s and 0.0018 mol/s)

[4 marks for correct answer, otherwise 1 mark for correctly drawn tangent to curve at 200 s, 1 mark for answer to 2 s.f., 1 mark for correct units]

4.3 The rate decreases ***[1 mark]***. This is because, as the amount of reactant A falls, so does its concentration and so the frequency of collisions between the reactant particles decreases ***[1 mark]***.

Pages 162-163 — Reversible Reactions

1.1 That the reaction is reversible / can go both ways ***[1 mark]***.

1.2 At equilibrium, the rate of the forward reaction is equal to the rate of the backwards reaction ***[1 mark]***.

2.1 It will be exothermic ***[1 mark]***. The same amount of energy will be released in the reverse reaction as is taken in by the forward reaction ***[1 mark]***.

2.2 The system has reached equilibrium ***[1 mark]***. This mixture contains both blue copper(II) ions and the yellow copper compound, so the colours mix to form green ***[1 mark]***.

2.3 E.g. by changing the temperature / by changing the concentration of one of the reactants ***[2 marks — 1 mark for each correct answer]***.

3.1 At time A, some of the methanol was removed from the reaction, lowering the concentration present ***[1 mark]***. As the reaction continued, more methanol was produced, increasing the concentration present in the reaction ***[1 mark]***.

3.2 The forward reaction must be exothermic ***[1 mark]***, as the equilibrium shifts to favour the reverse reaction in order to lower the temperature of the reaction ***[1 mark]***.

3.3 At time B, the pressure of the system was increased ***[1 mark]***. This shifted the equilibrium in the direction of the side with fewer moles, favouring the forward reaction and therefore decreasing the concentration of the reactants ***[1 mark]***.

3.4

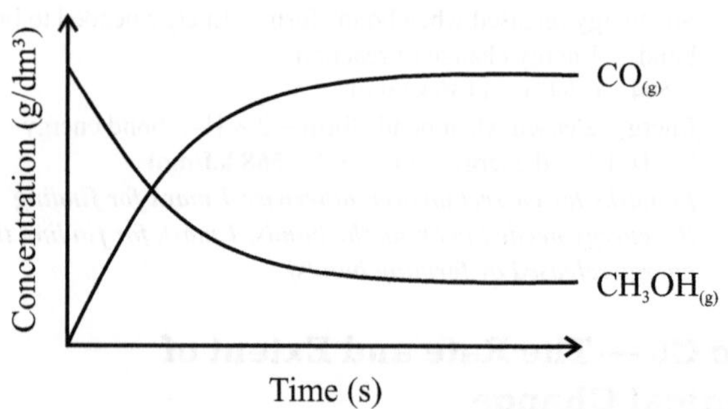

[1 mark for the correct curves, 1 mark for the correct labels]

Pages 164-165 — Le Chatelier's Principle

Warm-up

more reactants
more reactants
more products

1.1 If you change the conditions of a reversible reaction at equilibrium, the system will try to counteract that change ***[1 mark]***.

1.2 E.g. the temperature / the concentration of the reactants ***[2 marks — 1 mark for each correct answer]***

2.1 At higher temperatures there will be more ICl and less ICl_3 / the equilibrium will shift to the left ***[1 mark]***. This is because the reverse reaction is endothermic so opposes the increase in temperature ***[1 mark]***.

2.2 There would be more ICl_3 and less ICl ***[1 mark]*** because the increase in pressure ***[1 mark]*** causes the equilibrium position to move to the side with the fewest molecules of gas ***[1 mark]***.

3.1 At higher temperature there's more product (brown NO_2) in the equilibrium mixture ***[1 mark]***. This suggests that the equilibrium has moved to the right/forward direction ***[1 mark]***, so the forward reaction is endothermic ***[1 mark]***.

From Le Chatelier's principle, you know that increasing the temperature will favour the endothermic reaction as the equilibrium tries to oppose the change. So the forward reaction must be endothermic, as there's more NO_2 in the equilibrium mixture at higher temperatures.

3.2 The mixture would go a darker brown ***[1 mark]***, as the decrease in pressure causes the equilibrium to move to the side with the most molecules of gas ***[1 mark]***, meaning more NO_2 is formed ***[1 mark]***.

4 Observation 1: Increasing amounts of red $FeSCN^{2+}$ are formed, so the solution becomes a darker red ***[1 mark]***. When equilibrium is reached, the amount of each substance stops changing, and so does the colour ***[1 mark]***.
Observation 2: The concentration of Fe^{3+} initially increases, so the solution becomes more orangey ***[1 mark]***. The equilibrium then shifts to make more $FeSCN^{2+}$, so the solution becomes darker red in colour ***[1 mark]***.
Observation 3: The concentration of $FeSCN^{2+}$ initially increases, so the solution becomes darker red ***[1 mark]***.
The equilibrium then shifts to produce more reactants, so the solution becomes more orangey ***[1 mark]***.

Topic C7 — Organic Chemistry

Pages 166-167 — Hydrocarbons

Warm-up

Hydrocarbon	Not a hydrocarbon
propane	butanoic acid
ethene	CH_3CH_2Cl
C_2H_6	hydrochloric acid
C_2H_4	

1.1 A compound that is formed from hydrogen and carbon atoms only ***[1 mark]***.

1.2 butane, propane, ethane, methane ***[1 mark]***

1.3 C_nH_{2n+2} ***[1 mark]***

1.4 hydrocarbon + oxygen → **carbon dioxide** + **water** ***[1 mark]***

1.5 oxidised ***[1 mark]***

2.1 **B** ***[1 mark]***

2.2 **B**, **D**, and **E** ***[1 mark]***. They have the general formula C_nH_{2n+2} ***[1 mark]***.

2.3 **E** ***[1 mark]***. Boiling point increases with increasing molecular size/number of carbons ***[1 mark]***.

3.1 Diesel will be more viscous than petrol ***[1 mark]***. The higher boiling point of diesel means it contains larger molecules/ molecules with longer chains ***[1 mark]***.

3.2 Petrol ***[1 mark]***. The lower boiling point of petrol means it contains smaller molecules/molecules with shorter chains ***[1 mark]***.

3.3 $C_{20}H_{42}$ ***[1 mark]***

3.4 $\mathbf{2C_8H_{18} + 25O_2 \rightarrow 16CO_2 + 18H_2O}$ ***[1 mark for correct formulas of products, 1 mark for balancing]***

Any correct balance of the equation is correct, e.g. $C_8H_{18} + 12½O_2 \rightarrow 8CO_2 + 9H_2O$.

Page 168 — Fractional Distillation

1.1 The remains of ancient organisms/plankton ***[1 mark]***.

1.2 A resource which is being used quicker than it is being replaced so will run out eventually ***[1 mark]***.

1.3 alkanes ***[1 mark]***

2.1 boiling point ***[1 mark]***

2.2 The fractionating column is hot at the bottom and cool at the top ***[1 mark]***. So longer hydrocarbons, which have higher boiling points, will condense and be drained off near the bottom ***[1 mark]***. Meanwhile, shorter hydrocarbons, with lower boiling points, will condense and be drained off further up the column ***[1 mark]***.

2.3 They contain similar numbers of carbon atoms / they have a similar chain length ***[1 mark]***.

Pages 169-171 — Uses and Cracking of Crude Oil

1.1 Any two from: e.g. solvents / lubricants / polymers / detergents ***[2 marks — 1 mark for each correct answer]***

1.2 cracking ***[1 mark]***

1.3 E.g. shorter chain hydrocarbons are more useful/can be used for more applications ***[1 mark]***.

2.1 thermal decomposition / endothermic ***[1 mark]***

2.2 Hydrocarbons are vaporised / heated to form gases ***[1 mark]***. The vapours are then passed over a hot catalyst / the vapours are mixed with steam and heated to very high temperatures ***[1 mark]***.

2.3 E.g. $C_{10}H_{22} \rightarrow C_7H_{16} + C_3H_6$ ***[1 mark]***

Cracking equations must always be balanced and have a shorter alkane and an alkene on the right-hand side.

3.1 C_7H_{16} ***[1 mark]***

3.2
```
  H H H H
  | | | |
H-C-C-C-C-H
  | | | |
  H H H H
```

[1 mark for correct number of carbons, 1 mark for correct displayed formula]

3.3 E.g. to produce polymers / as a starting material for other chemicals ***[1 mark]***.

4 How to grade your answer:
Level 0: Nothing written worth of credit ***[No marks]***.
Level 1: Basic outline of how some fractions are processed but lacking detail. Some mention of the uses of cracking products ***[1 to 2 marks]***.
Level 2: Reason for cracking explained and some detail given about the process. The uses of cracking products are covered in detail ***[3 to 4 marks]***.
Level 3: Reasons for cracking and the process of cracking are explained in detail, including an accurate balanced symbol or word equation. Examples given of the uses of the products of cracking ***[5 to 6 marks]***.

Here are some points your answer may include:

Reasons for cracking
There is a higher demand for short chain hydrocarbons as these make good fuels.
Long chain hydrocarbons are less useful than short chain hydrocarbons, so there is less demand for them.
Cracking helps the supply of short chain hydrocarbons to meet the demand.

Cracking process
The long chain hydrocarbons are heated and vaporised.
The vapours are passed over a hot catalyst / mixed with steam and heated to a high temperature so that they thermally decompose.
Any relevant word equation: e.g. decane → octane + ethene
Any relevant balanced equation:
e.g. $C_{12}H_{26} \rightarrow C_8H_{18} + 2C_2H_4$

Uses of cracking products
The products of cracking are useful as fuels.
Alkenes are used as a starting material when making lots of other compounds and can be used to make polymers.

5.1 The hydrocarbon is very flammable ***[1 mark]***.
The bung prevents hydrocarbon vapour from escaping the boiling tube and igniting ***[1 mark]***.

5.2 E.g. they didn't completely fill the test tube with water at the start of the experiment *[1 mark]*.

5.3 E.g. the test tube could be replaced with a measuring cylinder *[1 mark]*.

5.4 If cold water was sucked back into the hot boiling tube, it could cause the boiling tube to crack *[1 mark]*.

5.5 It would not be safe/possible to reach the temperature required to conduct this reaction in a laboratory without a catalyst *[1 mark]*.

Topic C8 — Chemical Analysis

Page 172 — Purity and Formulations

1.1 A single element or compound not mixed with any other substance *[1 mark]*.

1.2 Sample **A** *[1 mark]*. The purer the substance, the smaller the range of the melting point / purer substances melt at higher temperatures than impure substances *[1 mark]*.

1.3 Sample **A** *[1 mark]*.

2.1 It is a mixture that has been designed to have a precise purpose *[1 mark]*. Each of the components is present in a measured quantity *[1 mark]* and contributes to the properties of the formulation *[1 mark]*.

2.2 By making sure each component in the mixture is always present in exactly the same quantity *[1 mark]*.

2.3 Any one from: e.g. medicines / cleaning products / fuels / cosmetics / fertilisers / metal alloys *[1 mark]*.

Pages 173-175 — Paper Chromatography

Warm-up

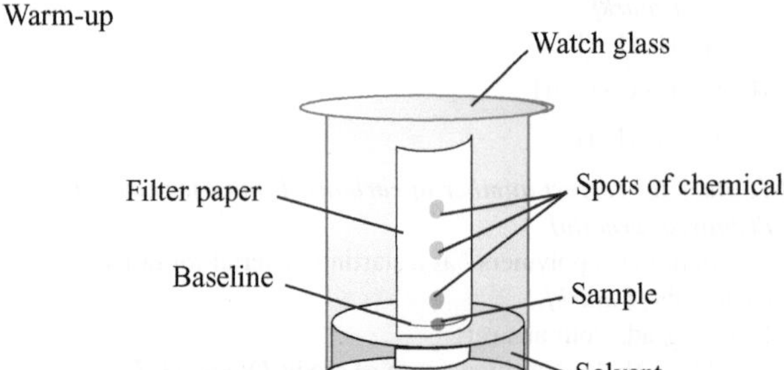

1.1 **E**: $R_f = \frac{\text{distance travelled by substance}}{\text{distance travelled by solvent}} = \frac{3.6}{9.5} = \mathbf{0.38}$

[2 marks for correct answer, otherwise 1 mark for using correct equation to calculate R_f]

F: $R_f = \frac{\text{distance travelled by substance}}{\text{distance travelled by solvent}} = \frac{8.0}{9.5} = \mathbf{0.84}$

[2 marks for correct answer, otherwise 1 mark for using correct equation to calculate R_f]

1.2 E.g. they're distributed differently between the mobile phase and the stationary phase *[1 mark]*.

1.3 They're all pure substances *[1 mark]*.

1.4 **D** and **E** *[1 mark]*.

2.1 E.g. to stop any solvent evaporating *[1 mark]*.

2.2 **A** spends more time in the mobile phase compared to the stationary phase than **B** does *[1 mark]*.

2.3 **B** and **C** *[1 mark]*.

2.4 The student is incorrect *[1 mark]*. Substances have different R_f values in different solvents as the attraction between the substance and solvent changes *[1 mark]*.

2.5 It suggest that there are at least 3 substances in **W** *[1 mark]*.

2.6 There were only two spots in the chromatogram shown because two of the substances in **W** are similarly distributed between the mobile phase/water and stationary phase / they had similar R_f values *[1 mark]*.

3.1 There are at least five compounds in the ink *[1 mark]* because there are 5 spots on the chromatogram *[1 mark]*. There is at least one insoluble compound *[1 mark]*, because there is still a spot on the baseline *[1 mark]*.

The student can't know exactly how many compounds are in the ink, as some compounds may not be soluble in the solvent, and others may have similar R_f values so their spots will overlap.

3.2 The student drew line A from the baseline to the top of the spot *[1 mark]*. They should have drawn the line to the centre of the spot *[1 mark]*. The student drew line B from the baseline to the top of the paper *[1 mark]*. They should have drawn line B from the baseline to the solvent front *[1 mark]*.

Page 176 — Tests for Gases

1.1 litmus paper *[1 mark]*.

1.2 chlorine/Cl_2 *[1 mark]*

2.1 E.g. the gas could be toxic/an irritant *[1 mark]*

2.2 Bubble the gas through limewater *[1 mark]*. If the gas is carbon dioxide, the limewater will turn cloudy *[1 mark]*.

2.3 The gas was not hydrogen *[1 mark]*.

2.4 oxygen *[1 mark]*

Topic C9 — Chemistry of the Atmosphere

Pages 177-178 — The Evolution of the Atmosphere

Warm-up

1 False

2 True

3 True

4 False

1.1 One-fifth oxygen and four-fifths nitrogen *[1 mark]*.

1.2 Any two from: e.g. carbon dioxide / water vapour / named noble gas *[2 marks — 1 mark for each correct answer]*

1.3 By algae and plants photosynthesising *[1 mark]*.

1.4 By volcanic activity *[1 mark]*.

1.5 200 million years *[1 mark]*

2.1 E.g. photosynthesis by plants and algae / carbon dioxide dissolved in the oceans *[1 mark]*.

2.2 From matter that is buried and compressed over millions of years *[1 mark]*.

2.3 Coal: from thick plant deposits *[1 mark]*.
Limestone: from calcium carbonate deposits from the shells and skeletons of marine organisms *[1 mark]*.

3.1 E.g. the long timescale means there's a lack of evidence *[1 mark]*.

3.2 $6CO_2 + 6H_2O \rightarrow C_6H_{12}O_6 + 6O_2$ *[1 mark]*

3.3 Oxygen is produced by photosynthesis *[1 mark]* and there are no plants or algae / there isn't any photosynthesis *[1 mark]* on Mars.

3.4 The fact that the red beds formed about 2 billion years ago suggests that before this time there wasn't enough oxygen in the air for iron oxide to form / from this time there was enough oxygen in the air for iron oxide to form *[1 mark]*.

Pages 179-181 — Greenhouse Gases and Climate Change

1.1 Nitrogen *[1 mark]*

1.2 They help to keep Earth warm *[1 mark]*.

1.3 Any two from: e.g. deforestation / burning fossil fuels / agriculture / producing waste *[2 marks — 1 mark for each correct answer]*

2.1 Greenhouse gases absorb long-wave (thermal) radiation *[1 mark]* reflected from Earth's surface *[1 mark]*. They then reradiate this thermal radiation in all directions, including back towards Earth, helping to warm the atmosphere *[1 mark]*.

2.2 E.g. flooding *[1 mark]* and coastal erosion *[1 mark]*.

2.3 Any one from: e.g. changes in rainfall patterns / the ability of certain regions to produce food might be affected / the frequency/severity of storms might increase / the distribution of wild species might change *[1 mark]*.

3 How to grade your answer:

Level 0: There is no relevant information *[No marks]*.

Level 1: Unstructured and no logic. The trends in the variables are described but reasons are not given *[1 to 2 marks]*.

Level 2: Some structure and logic but lacking clarity. The trends in the variables are described and there is some explanation of how the increase in carbon dioxide may have come about and how this might be linked to temperature *[3 to 4 marks]*.

Level 3: Clear, logical answer. The trends in the variables are described and there is a clear explanation of how the increase in carbon dioxide may have come about and how this may be linked to temperature ***[5 to 6 marks]***.

Here are some points your answer may include:
The graph shows an increase in carbon dioxide levels in the atmosphere between 1960 and 2015.
The increase in carbon dioxide levels is likely to be due to human activities which release carbon dioxide into the atmosphere.
These activities include increased burning of fossil fuels, increased deforestation and increased waste production.
The graph shows that the increase in carbon dioxide appears to correlate with an increase in global temperatures.
The increase in global temperatures is likely to be due to the increase in carbon dioxide in the atmosphere, as carbon dioxide is a greenhouse gas so helps to keep Earth warm.

4.1 The global warming potential for methane is significantly greater than for carbon dioxide ***[1 mark]***.
4.2 It has a very high global warming potential compared to other gases ***[1 mark]*** and stays in the atmosphere for a long time ***[1 mark]***.
5.1 E.g. the composition of the gases in the bubbles could be analysed to find out the concentration of greenhouse gases in the atmosphere at different times ***[1 mark]***.
5.2 The data does support the scientist's conclusion ***[1 mark]***. The global temperature anomaly, and therefore the global temperature, increases as the concentration of carbon dioxide increases ***[1 mark]***.
5.3 E.g. increasing carbon dioxide levels in the atmosphere cause the global temperature to increase ***[1 mark]***. Higher temperatures may cause ice caps to melt ***[1 mark]***, reducing the amount of ice available for scientists to collect ***[1 mark]***.
5.4 Any one from: e.g. collecting large ice cores is expensive / drilling so deep might disturb the local environment / scientists may require specialist equipment to collect/store large ice cores ***[1 mark]***.

Page 182 — Carbon Footprints

1.1 A measure of the amount of carbon dioxide and other greenhouse gases ***[1 mark]*** released over the full life cycle of something ***[1 mark]***.
1.2 Any two from: e.g. using renewable or nuclear energy sources / using more energy efficient appliances ***[2 marks — 1 mark for each correct answer]***.
1.3 E.g. lack of education / reluctance to change their lifestyle / cost of changing lifestyle ***[1 mark]***.
2.1 Any two from, e.g: specialist equipment is needed to capture the carbon dioxide / it's expensive to capture and store the carbon dioxide / it could be difficult to find suitable places to store the carbon dioxide ***[2 marks — 1 mark for each correct answer]***.
2.2 E.g. governments could tax companies based on the amount of greenhouse gases they emit ***[1 mark]***. They could also put a cap on the emissions produced by a company ***[1 mark]***. Governments might be reluctant to impose these methods if they think it will affect economic growth / could impact on people's well-being ***[1 mark]***, especially if other countries aren't using these methods either / the country is still developing ***[1 mark]***.

Page 183 — Air Pollution

1.1 Coal can contain sulfur impurities ***[1 mark]***
1.2 Acid rain: sulfur dioxide / nitrogen oxides/nitrogen monoxide/ nitrogen dioxide/dinitrogen monoxide ***[1 mark]***
Global dimming: e.g. (carbon) particulates ***[1 mark]***
1.3 Any two from: e.g. damage to plants / buildings / statues / corrodes metals ***[2 marks — 1 mark for each correct answer]***.
2.1 The reaction of nitrogen and oxygen from the air ***[1 mark]*** at the high temperatures produced by combustion ***[1 mark]***.
2.2 Nitrogen oxides cause respiratory problems ***[1 mark]*** and contribute to acid rain ***[1 mark]***.
2.3 E.g. they can cause respiratory problems ***[1 mark]***.
2.4 Carbon monoxide ***[1 mark]***. It is colourless and odourless ***[1 mark]***.

Topic C10 — Using Resources

Page 184 — Finite and Renewable Resources

1.1 Coal ***[1 mark]***. It does not form fast enough to be considered replaceable ***[1 mark]***.
1.2 A resource that reforms at a similar rate to, or faster, than humans can use it ***[1 mark]***.
2.1 E.g. the development of fertilisers has meant higher yields of crops ***[1 mark]***.
2.2 Any one from: e.g. synthetic rubber has replaced natural rubber / poly(ester) has replaced cotton in clothes / bricks are used instead of timber in construction ***[1 mark]***.
3 Any one advantage from: e.g. allows useful products to be made / provides jobs / brings money into the area ***[1 mark]***. Any one disadvantage: e.g. uses large amounts of energy / scars the landscape / produces lots of waste / destroys habitats ***[1 mark]***.

Pages 185-186 — Reuse and Recycling

1.1 An approach to development that takes account of the needs of present society ***[1 mark]*** while not damaging the lives of future generations ***[1 mark]***.
1.2 E.g. chemists can develop and adapt processes that use less resources/do less damage to the environment ***[1 mark]***. For example, chemists have developed catalysts that reduce the amount of energy required for industrial processes ***[1 mark]***.
2.1 The raw materials for the jute bag are more sustainable ***[1 mark]*** as plant fibres are a renewable resource, whilst crude oil is a finite resource ***[1 mark]***.
2.2 The production of the poly(ethene) bag is more sustainable ***[1 mark]*** as it needs less energy to be produced from its raw materials than the jute bag ***[1 mark]***.
2.3 The jute bag can be reused and the poly(ethene) bag can be recycled, improving both their sustainability ***[1 mark]***. However, the jute bag is more sustainable if the bags are disposed of in landfill ***[1 mark]***, as it is biodegradeable, whilst the poly(ethene) bag isn't ***[1 mark]***.
3.1 Any two from: e.g. often uses less energy / conserves the amount of raw materials on Earth / cuts down on waste sent to landfill ***[2 marks — 1 mark for each correct answer]***.
3.2 Any one from: e.g. glass / metal ***[1 mark]***
E.g. glass is crushed and melted down to form other glass products/other purpose / metal is melted and cast into the shape of a new product ***[1 mark]***.
3.3 reusing ***[1 mark]***
4.1 Plants are grown on soil containing copper compounds ***[1 mark]***, so as they grow, copper builds up in their leaves ***[1 mark]***. The plants are burned ***[1 mark]***. The resulting ash contains the copper compounds ***[1 mark]***.
4.2 By electrolysis of a solution containing the copper compounds ***[1 mark]*** or by displacement using scrap iron ***[1 mark]***.
4.3 Copper is a finite resource ***[1 mark]*** and will eventually run out ***[1 mark]***. Recycling copper makes it more sustainable ***[1 mark]***.

Pages 187-188 — Life Cycle Assessments

Warm-up
Getting the Raw Materials — Coal being mined from the ground.
Manufacturing and Packaging — Books being made from wood pulp.
Using the Product — A car using fuel while driving.
Product Disposal — Plastic bags going on to landfill.

1.1 Any two from: e.g. if a product is disposed of in landfill sites, it will take up space / may pollute land/water / energy is used to transport waste to landfill / pollution can be caused by incineration ***[2 marks — 1 mark for each correct answer]***.
1.2 Any one from: e.g. energy / water / some natural resources / certain types of waste ***[1 mark]***
1.3 They can be subjective / they are difficult to measure ***[1 mark]***.
1.4 No ***[1 mark]***. Some elements of the LCA are not objective/ require the assessors to make value judgements/cannot be quantified reliably ***[1 mark]***, therefore different people are likely to make a different judgement/estimate ***[1 mark]***.

1.5 Selective LCAs could be written so they only show elements that support a company's claims / they could be biased *[1 mark]* in order to give them positive advertising *[1 mark]*.

2.1 E.g. glass bottles can be reused multiple times, but cans are usually only used once *[1 mark]*.

2.2 It will positively affect their life cycle assessment *[1 mark]*. Using recycled aluminium to produce cans requires less energy than producing new cans, which means the manufacturing process will be cheaper *[1 mark]*.

2.3 Glass bottles have to be separated before they can be recycled *[1 mark]*. This will negatively affect the life cycle assessment for the glass bottles because e.g. it makes the recycling process more expensive and time-consuming to complete / some batches might need to be discarded because they are contaminated *[1 mark]*.

2.4 Any one from: e.g. how likely they are to be recycled / how easy/expensive it is to recycle them / the environmental costs of disposal if they are sent to landfill / their biodegradability *[1 mark]*

Pages 189-190 — Potable Water

Warm-up

1 False

2 True

3 False

1.1 pure water *[1 mark]*

1.2 e.g. from the ground / lakes / rivers *[1 mark]*.

1.3 passing water through filter beds — solid waste *[1 mark]*
sterilisation — microbes *[1 mark]*

1.4 E.g. chlorine, ozone, ultraviolet light *[3 marks — 1 mark for each correct answer]*.

2.1 **A**: Bunsen burner *[1 mark]*
B: round bottom flask *[1 mark]*
C: thermometer *[1 mark]*
D: condenser *[1 mark]*

2.2 Pour the salt water into the flask and secure it on top of a tripod *[1 mark]*. Connect the condenser to a supply of cold water *[1 mark]* that goes in at the bottom and out at the top *[1 mark]*. Heat the flask and allow the water to boil *[1 mark]*. Collect the water running out of the condenser in a beaker *[1 mark]*.

2.3 Reverse osmosis / a method which uses membranes *[1 mark]*

2.4 Desalination requires a lot of energy compared to the filtration and sterilisation of fresh water *[1 mark]*. Since the UK has a plentiful supply of fresh water there is no need to use desalination processes *[1 mark]*.

Page 191 — Waste Water Treatment

1.1 organic matter, harmful microbes *[2 marks — 1 mark for each correct answer]*

1.2 It may contain harmful chemicals which need to be removed *[1 mark]*.

2.1 To remove grit *[1 mark]* and large bits of material/twigs/plastic bags *[1 mark]*.

2.2 Substance **A**: sludge *[1 mark]*
Substance **B**: effluent *[1 mark]*

2.3 anaerobic digestion *[1 mark]*

Topic P1 — Energy

Page 192 — Energy Stores and Systems

1.1 An object or a group of objects. *[1 mark]*

1.2 Energy is transferred from: apple's gravitational potential energy store / apple's kinetic energy store *[1 mark]*
Energy is transferred to: apple's kinetic energy store / thermal energy store of the apple and surroundings (as the apple hits the ground) *[1 mark]*

1.3 E.g. work being done by the current in the circuit *[1 mark]*.

2 Level 0: There is no relevant information. *[No marks]*
Level 1: There is a brief explanation of one of the energy transfers, with no mention of the forces doing the work. *[1 to 2 marks]*
Level 2: There is a clear description of the energy transfers that take place, as well as the forces that are doing the work. *[3 to 4 marks]*

Here are some points your answer may include:
Gravitational force does work on the bike.
This causes energy to be transferred from the gravitational potential energy store of the bicycle to its kinetic energy store.
Friction force does work between the brake pads and the wheels.
This causes energy to be transferred from the bicycle's kinetic energy store to the thermal energy store of the brake pads.

Page 193 — Kinetic and Potential Energy Stores

1 $E_e = \frac{1}{2}ke^2 = \frac{1}{2} \times 20 \times 0.01^2$ *[1 mark]* = **0.001 J** *[1 mark]*

2 Energy lost from the g.p.e. store = energy gained in the kinetic energy store *[1 mark]*
$E_p = mgh = 0.1 \times 9.8 \times 0.45 = 0.441$ J *[1 mark]*
$E_k = \frac{1}{2}mv^2$
So $v = \sqrt{(2 \times E) \div m}$
$= \sqrt{(2 \times 0.441) \div 0.1}$ *[1 mark]*
= 2.969... *[1 mark]* = **3 m/s (to 1 s.f.)** *[1 mark]*

3.1 $E_e = \frac{1}{2}ke^2 = \frac{1}{2} \times 144 \times 0.10^2$ *[1 mark]* = 0.72 J
It is assumed that all of the energy stored in the elastic potential energy store of the elastic band is transferred to the kinetic energy store of the ball bearing ($E_e = E_k$)
so energy = **0.72 J** *[1 mark]*

3.2 Speed of child A's ball bearing:
$E_k = \frac{1}{2}mv^2 = 0.72$ J
so $v^2 = (2 \times 0.72) \div 0.0100 = 144$ *[1 mark]*
$v = 12$ m/s so child B's ball bearing speed is:
2×12 m/s = 24 m/s *[1 mark]*
$E_k = \frac{1}{2}mv^2 = \frac{1}{2} \times 0.0100 \times 24^2 = 2.88$ J *[1 mark]*
$E_e = \frac{1}{2}ke^2 = 2.88$ J
so $k = (2 \times 2.88) \div 0.10^2$ *[1 mark]*
= 576 = **580 N/m (to 2 s.f.)** *[1 mark]*

Pages 194-195 — Specific Heat Capacity

Warm-up

The energy needed to raise 1 kg of a substance by 1 °C.

1.1 $\Delta E = mc\Delta\theta$ so $c = \Delta E \div m\Delta\theta$ *[1 mark]*
$= 15\,000 \div (0.3 \times 25)$ *[1 mark]*
Specific heat capacity = **2000** *[1 mark]*

1.2 The current flowing through the immersion heater does work *[1 mark]*, transferring energy electrically *[1 mark]* to the thermal energy store of the immersion heater *[1 mark]*. It is then transferred from the thermal energy store of the immersion heater to the thermal energy store of the liquid *[1 mark]*.

2.2 Material C has the highest specific heat capacity *[1 mark]*. E.g. The higher the specific heat capacity of a material, the more energy is required to increase the temperature of 1 kg of the material by 1 °C *[1 mark]*. Material C had the smallest increase in temperature when the same amount of energy was transferred to the same mass of each material, so it must have the highest specific heat capacity *[1 mark]*.

You could also have answered this question using the specific heat capacity equation. $Q = mc\Delta\theta$, so the gradient of the graph is equal to $\frac{1}{mc}$. Since m is the same for all of the materials, this means the line with the shallowest gradient shows the highest specific heat capacity.

2.3 Valid results are repeatable and reproducible. To confirm that his results are repeatable, the student should repeat the experiment with the same method, and check that he gets very similar results *[1 mark]*. To confirm his results are reproducible, he should repeat the experiment using different equipment and/or a different experimental method, and check that he gets very similar results *[1 mark]*.

Pages 196-197 — Conservation of Energy and Power

Warm-up

Power is the **rate of** energy transfer or **work done**.
It is measured in **watts**.

1 E.g. energy transferred to a less useful energy store *[1 mark]*.

2.1 Energy can be created.
Energy can be destroyed.
[1 mark for both correct answers, otherwise no marks if more than two boxes have been ticked]

2.2 Useful energy store: e.g. kinetic energy store (of razor) ***[1 mark]***
Wasted energy store: e.g. thermal energy store (of shaver or surroundings) ***[1 mark]***

2.3 E.g. it would reduce the battery life of the battery / it would make the battery go flat quicker / it would mean the battery must be recharged more often ***[1 mark]***.

3.1 $P = W \div t$ ***[1 mark]***

3.2 $W = Pt = 35 \times 600$ ***[1 mark]*** = **21 000 J** ***[1 mark]***

3.3 $P = E \div t$
so $t = E \div P = 16\,800 \div 35$ ***[1 mark]*** = **480 s** ***[1 mark]***

4.1 It will decrease the time ***[1 mark]*** because more energy is being transferred to the kinetic energy store of the car per second ***[1 mark]*** so the car speeds up more quickly ***[1 mark]***.

4.2 The same amount of energy is needed to accelerate the car with both engines. The energy transferred by the old engine:
$P = E \div t$, so $E = P \times t = 32\,000 \times 9.0 = 288\,000$ J ***[1 mark]***
The time taken for the new engine to transfer the same amount of energy is:
$P = E \div t$, so $t = E \div P = 288\,000 \div 62\,000$
= 4.645... ***[1 mark]***
= **4.6 s (to 2 s.f.)** ***[1 mark]***

Pages 198-199 — Reducing Unwanted Energy Transfers

1.1 through the roof ***[1 mark]***

1.2 E.g. install loft insulation (to reduce convection) ***[1 mark]***

1.3 E.g. use draught excluders (to reduce convection) /
install double glazing (to reduce conduction) /
hang thick curtains (to reduce convection) / reduce the temperature difference between inside and outside the home
[1 mark for each sensible suggestion]

2 D ***[1 mark]***. The lower the rate of energy transfer through the brick, the more energy-efficient the house will be ***[1 mark]***.
D has a lower thermal conductivity value, so the rate of energy transfer through it will be lower ***[1 mark]***. It's also thicker (than brand B), which also reduces the rate of energy transfer through it ***[1 mark]***.

3 Doing work against friction causes energy to be dissipated/ wasted (usually to thermal energy stores) ***[1 mark]***. After lubricating the axle, the frictional forces acting on it were reduced ***[1 mark]***. This means that less energy is dissipated as the handle (and axle) is turned and so more energy is transferred to the kinetic energy store of the handle (and axle) and the bucket ***[1 mark]***.

4 Best: C Second best: B Worst: A ***[1 mark]***
The thicker a sample is, the slower the rate of energy transfer through it ***[1 mark]*** so sample B will be a better insulator than sample A ***[1 mark]***. Air has a lower thermal conductivity than glass (so it transfers energy at a slower rate than glass does) ***[1 mark]*** so even though samples B and C are the same thickness, sample C is a better insulator than sample B ***[1 mark]***.

Pages 200-201 — Efficiency

1.1 Efficiency = Useful output energy transfer
÷ Total input energy transfer ***[1 mark]***

1.2 Efficiency = 16 000 ÷ 20 000 ***[1 mark]***
= **0.8** ***[1 mark]***

You'd also get the mark for giving the efficiency as a percentage (80%).

2 Efficiency = 75% = 0.75
Efficiency = Useful power output ÷ Total power input
So Total power input = Useful power output ÷ Efficiency
[1 mark]
= 57 ÷ 0.75 ***[1 mark]*** = **76 W** ***[1 mark]***

3.1 Useful output power of the air blower:
Efficiency = Useful power output ÷ Total power input
so Useful power output = Efficiency × Total power input
= 0.62 × 533 ***[1 mark]***
= 330.46 W ***[1 mark]***
Useful power output of the turbine:
Efficiency = 13% = 0.13
Total power input = Useful power of air blower
Useful power output = Efficiency × Total power input
= 0.13 × 330.46 ***[1 mark]***
= 42.9598
= **43 W (to 2 s.f.)** ***[1 mark]***

3.2 E.g. adding more sails (so there is a larger surface area for the air to hit) / increasing the size of the sails (so there is a larger surface area for the air to hit) / adding a lubricant to the moving parts of the turbine (to reduce friction) / changing the angle of the sails so they get hit by more wind ***[2 marks — 1 mark for each sensible suggestion]***

4.1 E.g. the student could measure the temperature of the water in the kettle, so that they can be sure they measure the energy transferred to increase the water's temperature to 100 °C (not any more or less) ***[1 mark]***.

4.2 The student will record an inaccurate value of energy transferred to the kettle for this reading ***[1 mark]***. This is because some of the residual energy in the kettle's thermal energy store from the previous trial will be transferred to the water and begin to increase its temperature, so less energy will need to be transferred from the power supply to boil the water ***[1 mark]***.

4.3 The results are not consistent with the prediction.
By calculating the efficiencies at different volumes from the data in Table 1, using efficiency = $\frac{\text{useful energy output}}{\text{total energy input}}$
[1 mark], it can be seen that:
E.g. for 660 cm^3 of water, efficiency = 0.168 ÷ 0.212
= 0.792... ***[1 mark]***,
while for 2000 cm^3 of water, efficiency = 0.504 ÷ 0.547
= 0.921... ***[1 mark]***.
Therefore, the efficiency of the kettle was greater for a larger volume of water than a smaller volume (the opposite of the student's prediction) ***[1 mark]***.

You don't have to have done the exact same calculations we have here. As long as you've come to the right conclusion and have done some calculations to show that efficiency is larger for a bigger volume than a smaller volume,. you'll get the marks.

Pages 202-203 — Energy Resources and Their Uses

Warm-up

Renewable — bio-fuel, solar, tidal, geothermal, wave power, hydroelectricity, wind
Non-renewable — oil, coal, gas, nuclear fuel

1 E.g. a non-renewable energy resource will one day run out ***[1 mark]*** but a renewable energy resource can be replenished as it is used ***[1 mark]***.

2.1 coal, oil, (natural) gas ***[1 mark]***

2.2 E.g. generating electricity / burning coal on fires / using gas central heating / using a gas fire / coal in steam trains
[2 marks — 1 for each correct answer]

2.3 Bio-fuels are solids, liquids or gases that are produced from plant products or from animal waste ***[1 mark]***.

2.4 E.g. because fossil fuels will eventually run out / because fossil fuels harm the environment ***[1 mark for any correct answer]***.

3 E.g. during winter, there are fewer hours of daylight, but the weather is usually more windy ***[1 mark]***, so wind turbines will be able to generate more electricity during winter ***[1 mark]***. However, during the summer, there will be more daylight hours and the weather will be less windy ***[1 mark]***, so solar panels will be more favourable ***[1 mark]***. By installing both, the university will have a more reliable electricity supply throughout the year ***[1 mark]***.

4.1 How to grade your answer:
Level 0: There is no relevant information. ***[No marks]***
Level 1: There is a brief description of the reliability or environmental impact of one of the energy resources. ***[1 to 2 marks]***
Level 2: There is a clear and detailed description of the reliability and environmental impacts of both energy resources, as well as some similarities between them. ***[3 to 4 marks]***
Here are some points your answer may include:
Both energy resources are reliable.
Tides come in and out at known times.
Except in times of drought, there is always water available for a hydroelectric power plant to work.

Hydroelectric power plants require the flooding of valleys, which causes a loss of habitat for any animals living there.
The plants in the valley die during the flood and rot, which releases gases that contribute to global warming.
Using tides to generate electricity creates no pollution, but tidal barrages do alter the habitat of nearby animals.

4.2 How to grade your answer:
Level 0: There is no relevant information. ***[No marks]***
Level 1: There is a brief explanation of an advantage or a disadvantage of fossil fuels. ***[1 to 2 marks]***
Level 2: There is some explanation of both advantages and disadvantages of fossil fuels. ***[3 to 4 marks]***
Level 3: There is a clear and detailed explanation of the advantages and disadvantages of using fossil fuels. ***[5 to 6 marks]***

Here are some points your answer may include:
Advantages:
Fossil fuels are reliable.
They are extracted at a fast enough rate that there are always some in stock.
Power plants can respond quickly to peaks in demand.
Running costs of fossil fuel power plants aren't that expensive compared to other energy resources.
Fuel extraction costs are also low.
Disadvantages:
Fossil fuels are slowly running out / they are a non-renewable energy resource.
Burning fossil fuels releases carbon dioxide into the atmosphere.
Carbon dioxide in the atmosphere contributes to global warming.
Burning coal and oil also releases sulfur dioxide, which causes acid rain.
Acid rain can damage soil and trees. This can damage or destroy the habitats of animals.
Coal mining can spoil the view by damaging the landscape.
Oil spillages kill sea life and birds and mammals that live near to the sea.

Page 204 — Trends in Energy Resource Use

1.1 35 + 23 + 5 = 63 %
[2 marks for correct answer, otherwise 1 mark for reading all three values correctly from the graph]

1.2 E.g. the country is using a larger percentage renewable energy resources to generate electricity in 2015 than they were the previous year / overall, they are using a smaller percentage of fossil fuels to generate their electricity in 2015 than they were in 2014 ***[1 mark]***.

2 How to grade your answer:
Level 0: There is no relevant information. ***[No marks]***
Level 1: There is a brief explanation why the UK is using more renewable energy resources. ***[1 to 2 marks]***
Level 2: There is some explanation of why the UK is using more renewable energy resources and the factors that restrict the increase in their use. ***[3 to 4 marks]***
Level 3: There is a clear and detailed explanation of why the UK is using more renewable energy resources and the factors that restrict the increase in their use. ***[5 to 6 marks]***

Here are some points your answer may include:
Reasons the UK is using more renewable energy resources:
We understand more about the negative effects that fossil fuels have on the environment, so more people want to use renewable energy resources that have less of an impact on the environment.
Fossil fuel reserves will run out, so we have to find an alternative for them.
Pressure from the public and other countries has lead to government targets for the use of renewable energy resources.
This can lead to increased government funding for renewable energy resources.
Pressure from the public and the global community/other countries has also lead to private companies creating more environmentally-friendly products that use renewable energy resources.
Factors that limit the use of renewable energy resources:
Building new power plants to replace existing fossil fuel powered ones costs money.
Some renewable energy resources are less reliable than fossil fuels.
Research into improving renewable energy resources costs money and will take time.
Personal products that use renewable energy resources, like hybrid cars, are generally more expensive than similar ones that use fossil fuels.

Topic P2 — Electricity

Page 205 — Current and Circuit Symbols

Warm-up
A — cell, B — switch, C — filament lamp, D — fuse.

1.1 There is no source of potential difference ***[1 mark]***
1.2 Current is the rate of flow of **charge** ***[1 mark]***.
2.1 0.5 A ***[1 mark]***
Remember that the current is the same at any point in a single closed circuit loop.
2.2 $Q = I \times t$ ***[1 mark]***
2.3 $t = 2 \times 60 = 120$ s
Charge = 0.5 × 120 ***[1 mark]***
= **60** ***[1 mark]*** **C** ***[1 mark]***

Page 206 — Resistance and V = IR

1 $V = I \times R$
$V = 3 \times 6$ ***[1 mark]*** = **18 V** ***[1 mark]***

2.1 She could have varied the length of the wire between the crocodile clips ***[1 mark]*** and divided the reading on the voltmeter by the reading on the ammeter to find the resistance for each length ***[1 mark]***.

2.2
Resistance (Ω)
3.0 2.5 2.0 1.5 1.0 0.5 0
0 10 20 30 40 50
Length (cm)

[1 mark for resistance on vertical axis and length on horizontal axis, 1 mark for appropriate values labelled on both axes, 1 mark for correctly plotted points, 1 mark for suitable line of best fit.]

2.3 The resistance is proportional to the length ***[1 mark]***. This is shown by the graph being a straight line through the origin ***[1 mark]***.

Pages 207-209 — Resistance and I-V Characteristics

1.1 C ***[1 mark]***
At a constant temperature, the relationship between pd and current is linear — when this is true, the resistor is said to be ohmic.
1.2 I-V characteristic ***[1 mark]***
1.3 A resistor at a constant temperature is an example of an **ohmic** conductor. It is also an example of a **linear** component.
[1 mark for each correct answer]

2.1
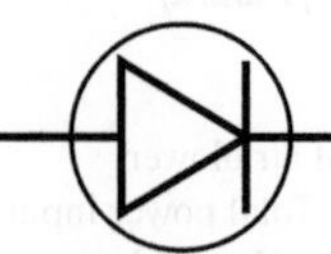
[1 mark]

2.2 A diode only lets current flow through it in one direction ***[1 mark]***.
2.3 The student put the diode/power supply in the circuit the other

way around *[1 mark]*. The resistance of a diode is very large when current goes through it one way and very small when current goes through in the opposite direction *[1 mark]*.

3.1 It is used to alter the current *[1 mark]* so the potential difference can be measured for each current *[1 mark]*.

3.2 At 3 A the pd is 12 V *[1 mark]*
$V = I \times R$
$R = V \div I$ *[1 mark]* $= 12 \div 3$ *[1 mark]* $=$ **4 Ω** *[1 mark]*

3.3 The resistance increases as the current increases *[1 mark]*. This is because the increase in current causes the temperature to rise *[1 mark]*.

3.4 A resistor is ohmic when the relationship between current and potential difference is linear *[1 mark]*. The graph is linear until approximately 3.5 V, so the resistor is ohmic in this range *[1 mark]*.

4.1 E.g. adjust the variable resistor to change the current through the circuit. Record the current through the diode using the ammeter, and the potential difference across it using the voltmeter *[1 mark]*. Use the equation $V = IR$ (in the form $R = V \div I$) to calculate the resistance of the diode at this current using the current and potential difference measurements *[1 mark]*. Repeat this for a number of different values of current (e.g. at least 6), changing the current by a fixed amount each time (e.g. 1 mA) *[1 mark]*.

4.2 E.g.

[1 mark for smooth line passing through or close to all points]

4.3 E.g. she has only carried out the experiment for positive values of current / current flowing in one direction *[1 mark]*. This means she cannot make a conclusion about the effect of the size of the current, because the device may behave differently for current that flows in the opposite direction / because diodes are known to have a very high resistance for one direction of current flow but not the opposite *[1 mark]*.

Page 210 — Circuit Devices

1.1

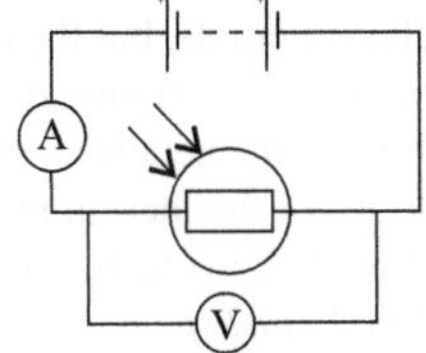

[1 mark for correct LDR symbol, 1 mark for LDR, ammeter and power supply in series, 1 mark for voltmeter in parallel across LDR.]

1.2 It decreases *[1 mark]*

1.3 E.g. automatic night lights / burglar detectors *[1 mark]*

2 As the temperature increases, the resistance of the thermistor decreases *[1 mark]*. This means the current in the circuit increases *[1 mark]*. As the current increases, the brightness of the light increases *[1 mark]*. When the cooker's surface is cold, the resistance is high and the current is too small to light the bulb *[1 mark]*.

Page 211 — Series Circuits

1 A *[1 mark]*.

In a series circuit, there should only be one closed loop of wire.

2.1 $10 + 30 =$ **40 Ω** *[1 mark]*

2.2 $V = I \times R$
$V = 75 \times 10^{-3} \times 30$ *[1 mark]* $=$ **2.25 V** *[1 mark]*

3 The potential difference across the 8 Ω resistor is:
$6 - 2 = 4$ V *[1 mark]*
$V = I \times R$, so the current through the 8 Ω resistor is:
$I = V \div R = 4 \div 8$ *[1 mark]* $= 0.5$ A *[1 mark]*
This is the same as the current through R, so the resistance of R is: $R = V \div I = 2 \div 0.5$ *[1 mark]* $=$ **4 Ω** *[1 mark]*

Page 212 — Parallel Circuits

1

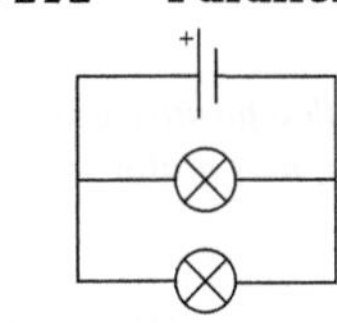

[1 mark]

2.1 6 V *[1 mark]*

Potential difference is the same across all components in parallel.

2.2 $V = IR$ so $I = V \div R$ *[1 mark]*
A_1: $I = V \div R = 6 \div 4$ *[1 mark]* $=$ **1.5 A** *[1 mark]*
A_2: $I = V \div R = 6 \div 12$ *[1 mark]* $=$ **0.5 A** *[1 mark]*

2.3 The current from the supply splits into 1.5 A and 0.5 A.
So A_3 reads $1.5 + 0.5 =$ **2 A** *[1 mark]*

3 How to grade your answer:

Level 0: There is no relevant information. ***[No marks]***

Level 1: There is a brief explanation about the effect of adding resistors in series or parallel. ***[1 to 2 marks]***

Level 2: There is a comparison between adding resistors in series and parallel and an explanation of their effects. ***[3 to 4 marks]***

Level 3: A logical and detailed comparison is given, explaining why adding resistors in series increases the total resistance but adding them in parallel reduces it. ***[5 to 6 marks]***

Here are some points your answer may include:
In series, resistors share the potential difference from the power source.
The more resistors that are in series, the lower the potential difference for each one, and so the lower the current for each one.
Current is the same all around a series circuit, so adding a resistor will decrease the current for the whole circuit.
A decrease in total current means an increase in total resistance.
In parallel, all resistors have the same potential difference as the source.
Adding another resistor in parallel (forming another circuit loop) increases the current flowing in the circuit, as there are more paths for the current to flow through.
An increase in total current means a decrease in total resistance (because $V = IR$).

Page 213 — Investigating Resistance

1.1

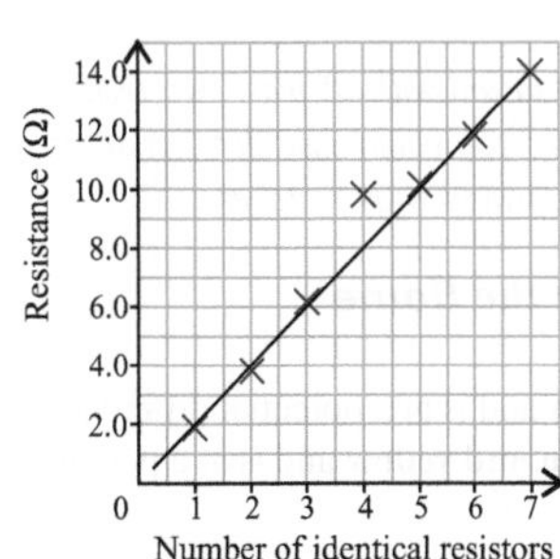

Resistance = **8.0 Ω**

[1 mark for a straight line of best fit that excludes the point plotted for 4 resistors, 1 mark for correct prediction of resistance]

1.2

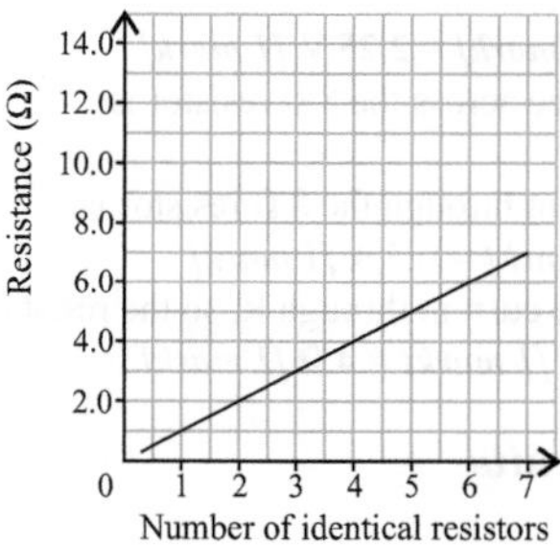

[1 mark for a straight line of best fit with a positive gradient, 1 mark for the gradient of the line being half of the gradient of the line drawn in 1.1]

2 How to grade your answer:

Level 0: There is no relevant information. ***[No marks]***

Level 1: There is a brief description of the techniques used to measure resistance of the circuit. The steps mentioned are not in a logical order. ***[1 to 2 marks]***

Level 2: There is a good description of the techniques used to measure resistance of the circuit. Most steps are given in a logical order and they could be followed to produced valid results. A correct circuit diagram may be included. ***[3 to 4 marks]***

Level 3: A logical and detailed description is given, fully describing the method for investigating the effect of adding resistors in parallel. The method could easily be followed to produce valid results. A correct circuit diagram may be included. ***[5 to 6 marks]***

Here are some points your answer may include:
Connect a battery or cell in series with an ammeter and a fixed resistor.
Measure the source potential difference using the voltmeter.
Measure the current through the circuit using the ammeter.
Calculate the resistance of the circuit using $R = V \div I$.
Connect a second identical resistor in parallel with the first resistor.
Do not connect the second resistor across the ammeter.
Measure the current and use this to calculate the resistance of the circuit.
Repeat this for several identical resistors.
Plot a graph of number of identical resistors against overall resistance of the circuit.
A correct circuit diagram, similar to:

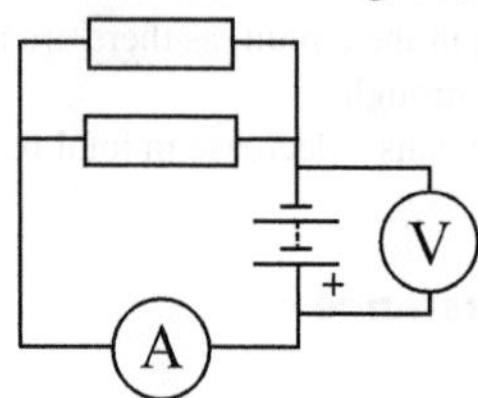

So long as you draw a correct diagram with at least two resistors in parallel, you would get the marks. You could also draw your circuit with several resistors in parallel, all separated with switches.

Page 214 — Electricity in the Home

Warm-up

The live wire is **brown** and is at a potential difference of **230** V. The earth wire is **green and yellow** and is at a potential difference of **0** V.

1.1 230 V ***[1 mark]***
50 Hz ***[1 mark]***

1.2 How to grade your answer:

Level 0: There is no relevant information. ***[No marks]***

Level 1: There is a brief explanation of the function of the live and neutral wires and some attempt at explaining why the toaster would not work. ***[1 to 2 marks]***

Level 2: There is a good explanation of the function of the live and neutral wires and why the fault would not allow a current to flow through the toaster. ***[3 to 4 marks]***

Here are some points your answer may include:
The purpose of the neutral wire is to complete the circuit.
Current flows into the toaster via the live wire, through the toaster, and out of the device by the neutral wire.
The fault means that a closed loop/low-resistance path has been formed between the live and neutral wire before the current in the live wire has reached the toaster.
So no (or very little) current will flow through the toaster.
This means that the toaster will not work.

2.1 To stop an electric current from flowing out of the live wire and potentially causing an electric shock (i.e. for safety) ***[1 mark]***. To make it easy to identify the live wire ***[1 mark]***.

2.2 The man has an electric potential of 0 V ***[1 mark]*** and the wire has an electric potential (of 230 V) so a potential difference exists between them ***[1 mark]***. This causes a current to flow through the man ***[1 mark]***.

2.3 Yes ***[1 mark]***. Although there is no current flowing when it is switched off, there is still a potential difference ***[1 mark]***, so touching the live wire in the socket could cause a current to flow through you to the Earth ***[1 mark]***.

Pages 215-216 — Power of Electrical Appliances

1 The **power** of an appliance is the energy transferred **per second**. Energy is transferred because the **current** does work against the appliance's resistance. ***[1 mark for each correct]***

2.1 $E = P \times t$ ***[1 mark]***

2.2 $E = 50 \times 20$ ***[1 mark]*** = **1000 J** ***[1 mark]***

2.3 The power of the car is higher ***[1 mark]***. So more energy is transferred away from the chemical energy store of the battery per second ***[1 mark]***.

3.1 Energy is transferred electrically from the power source ***[1 mark]*** to the thermal energy store of the water ***[1 mark]*** and the kinetic energy store of the motor ***[1 mark]***.

3.2 Work done = power × time ($E = P \times t$)
Work done = 400 × 60 ***[1 mark]*** = **24 000 J** ***[1 mark]***

3.3 Time of economy mode = 160 × 60 = 9600 s
Energy transferred in economy mode
= power × time = 400 × 9600 = 3 840 000 J ***[1 mark]***
Time of standard mode = 125 × 60 = 7500 s
Energy transferred in standard mode = 600 × 7500
= 4 500 000 J ***[1 mark]***
Energy saved = 4 500 000 – 3 840 000 ***[1 mark]***
= **660 000 J** ***[1 mark]***

4.1 How to grade your answer:

Level 0: There is no relevant information. ***[No marks]***

Level 1: There are some relevant points, but the answer is unclear. There is some description of the experimental set-up, but the details are unclear. There are explanations of the measurements and calculations that should be made, but they may be incomplete. ***[1 to 2 marks]***

Level 2: There is a clear description of how the equipment listed should be set up and used to carry out an experiment safely. There are full explanations of the measurements and calculations that should be made to determine the useful output power of the motor. ***[3 to 4 marks]***

Here are some points your answer may include:
Securely attach the clamp stand to the edge of a bench/worktop.
Set up the motor so that it is connected to the circuit, and clamped to the clamp stand. Make sure there is at least a metre of clear space between the motor and the ground.
Attach one end of the string to the axle of the motor (so that it will wind around the axle when the motor spins).
Attach the other end of the string to the 1 kg mass securely,

so it hangs from the string.
Set up the ruler to stand vertically, parallel to the string.
Attach a marker to the bottom of the mass so that the distance moved by the mass can be accurately measured.
Turn on the motor, and, using the stopwatch, record the time taken for the motor to lift the mass through a fixed vertical height, e.g. 60 cm, measured by the metre ruler.
Repeat this at least two more times, and calculate an average value of the time taken from the three results.
Use the height to calculate the change in gravitational potential energy of the mass, and so the useful energy transferred by the motor.
Calculate the useful power by dividing this value of energy by the average value of time taken.

4.2 0.01 s ***[1 mark]***.

4.3 The errors in the student's time measurements will mostly be caused by human error and her reaction time ***[1 mark]***. Human reaction times are typically much larger than the smallest time measured by the stopwatch (0.2-0.9 s compared to 0.01 s) ***[1 mark]***.

Page 217 — More on Power

Warm-up

A power source supplies **energy** to a charge. When a charge passes through a component with **resistance**, it does **work**, so the charge's energy **decreases**.

1.1 $E = V \times Q$ ***[1 mark]***

1.2 $E = 6 \times 2$ ***[1 mark]*** = **12 J** ***[1 mark]***

1.3 Multiplying the potential difference by the current gives the power ***[1 mark]***. In 1.2 the energy was transferred by the two coulombs of charge in one second ***[1 mark]***. This is the same as the power ***[1 mark]***.

2.1 $P = I \times V$
so $I = P \div V = 75 \div 230$ ***[1 mark]*** = 0.3260...
= **0.33 A (to 2 s.f.)** ***[1 mark]***

2.2 $P = I^2 \times R$
so $R = P \div I^2 = 2.5 \div 0.50^2$ ***[1 mark]*** = **10 Ω** ***[1 mark]***

Page 218 — The National Grid

1.1 Potential Difference ***[1 mark]***, Current ***[1 mark]***

1.2 A step-up transformer increases the potential difference, a step-down transformer decreases it ***[1 mark]***.

2.1 Transformer A = step-up transformer ***[1 mark]***
Transformer B = step-down transformer ***[1 mark]***

2.2 How to grade your answer:
Level 0: There is no relevant information. ***[No marks]***
Level 1: There is a brief explanation of the function of the step-up transformer and how this results in smaller energy losses. ***[1 to 2 marks]***
Level 2: There is a good explanation of the function of the step-up transformer and how reducing the energy lost increases the efficiency of the national grid. ***[3 to 4 marks]***

Here are some points your answer may include:
Transformer A increases the potential difference.
This decreases the current at a given power.
This decrease in current decreases energy lost to the thermal energy stores of the cables and surroundings.
Efficiency is useful output energy transfer ÷ total input energy transfer, so reducing the energy lost to thermal stores makes the transmission of electricity more efficient.

2.3 The potential difference across the power cables is very high and too large for domestic devices ***[1 mark]***. Transformer B reduces the potential difference to lower, usable levels ***[1 mark]***.

Topic P3 — Particle Model of Matter

Pages 219-220 — The Particle Model and Motion in Gases

Warm-up

From left to right: liquid, solid, gas

1 When the temperature of a gas increases, the average energy in the **kinetic** energy stores of the gas molecules increases. This **increases** the **average** speed of the gas molecules. If the gas is kept at a constant volume, increasing the temperature **increases** the pressure.
[3 marks for all correct, otherwise 1 mark for two correct or 2 marks for three correct]

2.1 There would be more air particles in the same volume ***[1 mark]***, so the particles would collide with the tyre walls (and each other) more often ***[1 mark]***. This would mean the pressure would increase ***[1 mark]***.

2.2 On a hot day, the air particles in the tyre would have more energy in their kinetic energy stores ***[1 mark]***, so they would move faster and hit the tyre walls more often ***[1 mark]***.
As the particles are moving faster, they also have a larger momentum, so the force each particle exerts on the tyre walls is larger ***[1 mark]***. Hitting the tyre walls with a greater force and more often creates a higher pressure ***[1 mark]***.

3 A ***[1 mark]***

The volume of each container is the same (0.04 m^3 = 40 000 cm^3). A fixed mass and volume of a gas has a lower pressure at a lower temperature.

4 The large lid will pop off first ***[1 mark]***. As the temperature of the gas increases, the particles have more energy in their kinetic energy stores. The momentum of the particles increases, so the force they exert on a unit area of the container walls increases ***[1 mark]***. The particles also hit the walls more often, which also increases the force acting on a unit area ***[1 mark]***. As the large lid as a larger area, the total force acting on it at any temperature will be higher than the total force acting on the smaller lid ***[1 mark]***. So the force required to remove one of the lids will be reached by the larger lid first ***[1 mark]***.

Pages 221-222 — Density of Materials

1.1 $\rho = m \div v$ ***[1 mark]***

1.2 $\rho = 10\ 000 \div 0.5$ ***[1 mark]*** = **20 000 kg/m^3** ***[1 mark]***

1.3 The density is the same for the whole block,
so $\rho = 20\ 000$ kg/m^3
$\rho = m \div v$
so $m = \rho \times v = 20\ 000 \times 0.02$ ***[1 mark]*** = **400 kg** ***[1 mark]***

2 Level 0: There is no relevant information. ***[No marks]***
Level 1: There is a brief description of the set-up of apparatus. There is no mention of how to measure volume or how to calculate density. ***[1 to 2 marks]***
Level 2: There is a detailed explanation of the set-up of apparatus, with a description of the measurements needed to be taken and how these are used to find the density. ***[3 to 4 marks]***

Here are some points your answer may include:
Place the empty beaker on the mass balance.
Zero the mass balance before putting acetic acid in the beaker.
Pour some acetic acid into the beaker.
Write down the mass of the acid shown on the mass balance.
Read the volume of the acid from the scale on the beaker.
Use the equation density = mass ÷ volume to calculate the density of the acetic acid.

3.1 First measure the mass of the object using a mass balance ***[1 mark]***. Then submerge the object in the water and measure the volume of water displaced ***[1 mark]***.
The volume of the displaced water in the measuring cylinder is equal to the volume of the object ***[1 mark]***.
Use density = mass ÷ volume to calculate the density of the object ***[1 mark]***.

3.2 $\rho = m \div v$
1 ml of water = 1 cm^3 ***[1 mark]***
A: $\rho = 5.7 \div 0.30 = 19$ g/cm^3. So A is gold. ***[1 mark]***
B: $\rho = 2.7 \div 0.60 = 4.5$ g/cm^3. So B is titanium. ***[1 mark]***
C: $\rho = 3.0 \div 0.30 = 10$ g/cm^3. So C is silver. ***[1 mark]***

4 Volume of empty aluminium can
= volume displaced by full can – volume of cola
= 337 – 332 = 5 ml ***[1 mark]***
5 ml = 5 cm^3 ***[1 mark]***
$\rho = m \div v$ = 13.5 ÷ 5 ***[1 mark]*** = **2.7 g/cm^3** ***[1 mark]***

Page 223 — Internal Energy and Changes of State

1 When a system is heated, the internal energy of the system **increases**. This either increases the **temperature** of the system or causes a change of state. During a change of state the temperature and **mass** of the substance remain constant.
[2 marks for all correct, otherwise 1 mark for two correct]

2.1 Gas to liquid: condensing
Liquid to gas: evaporating/boiling
[1 mark for both correct]

2.2 E.g. a change where you don't end up with a new substance / you end up with the same substance in a different form ***[1 mark]***.

3.1 E.g. the energy stored in a system by its particles. / The sum of the energy in the particles' kinetic and potential energy stores ***[1 mark]***.

3.2 Any two from: mass, specific heat capacity, total energy transferred to the system ***[2 marks]***

4 10 g ***[1 mark]*** E.g. because when a substance changes state, its mass doesn't change. So the mass of the water vapour equals the mass of the water originally in the test tube minus the mass of water left at the end ***[1 mark]***.

Pages 224-225 — Specific Latent Heat

1.1 The amount of energy required to change the state of one kilogram of a substance with no change in temperature ***[1 mark]***.

1.2 $E = mL$ so $L = E \div m$ ***[1 mark]***
L = 1.13 ÷ 0.5 ***[1 mark]*** = **2.26 MJ/kg** ***[1 mark]***

2.1 The substance is melting ***[1 mark]***.

2.2 As the substance is heated, its internal energy increases ***[1 mark]***. As the substance melts (during 3-8 minutes), all of this energy is used to break apart intermolecular bonds ***[1 mark]*** so there is no increase in the substance's temperature as it changes state ***[1 mark]***.

2.3 Melting point = –7 °C ***[1 mark]***
Boiling point = 58 °C ***[1 mark]***

3.1 Any two from: e.g. take temperature measurements at smaller time intervals / continue measuring after the first non-zero temperature measurement to be sure the ice has finished melting / find the mass of any remaining solid ice at the end of the experiment to determine the exact mass of ice that melted / use a temperature probe to automatically record temperature values at accurate times ***[2 marks]***.

3.2 Total energy required to melt the ice is given by $E = mL$
E = 0.05 × 334 000 = 16 700 J ***[1 mark]***
The time in which energy was transferred to the ice and only caused the ice to melt is given by the flat part of the graph, since this is where the temperature didn't change. The flat part of the graph starts at 3 minutes, and finishes at 142 minutes. So the total time for the flat section
= 142 – 3 = 139 minutes = 139 × 60 = 8340 s ***[1 mark]***
So, average rate of energy transfer
= total energy transferred ÷ time taken for energy transfer
= 16 700 ÷ 8340 ***[1 mark]*** = 2.002... = **2 J/s (to 1 s.f.)**
[1 mark]

3.3 The student is incorrect. For the second experiment to be a valid test of the experiment's repeatability, it has to be identical to the first experiment ***[1 mark]***. Since the student has used ice in a different form for the second experiment, the method and conditions are not the same, so the student cannot make conclusions about the first experiment's repeatability from the results ***[1 mark]***.

Topic P4 — Atomic Structure

Pages 226-227 — Developing the Model of the Atom

Warm-up
1 × 10^{-10} m
10 000

1.1 Our current model shows that the atom can be broken up (into protons, neutrons and electrons) ***[1 mark]***.

1.2 The plum pudding model ***[1 mark]***. This was where an atom was thought to be a sphere of positive charge, with electrons spread throughout it ***[1 mark]***.

1.3 The neutron ***[1 mark]***.

2.1 An electron can move into a higher energy level / further from the nucleus, by absorbing EM radiation ***[1 mark]***, and move into a lower energy level / closer to the nucleus, by emitting EM radiation ***[1 mark]***.

2.2 ion ***[1 mark]***

2.3 Positive (or +1) ***[1 mark]***

An atom is neutral. Losing an electron takes away negative charge, so the remaining ion is positive.

3 Level 0: There is no relevant information. ***[No marks]***
Level 1: There is only one correct discovery mentioned with a brief description of the observation that led to it. ***[1 to 2 marks]***
Level 2: Two correct discoveries are given with a detailed description of how observations led to them. ***[3 to 4 marks]***
Here are some points your answer may include:
Discovery: The atom is mostly made up of empty space / most of the atom's mass is concentrated at the centre in a tiny nucleus.
Observation: Most of the alpha particles fired at the thin gold foil passed straight through.
Discovery: The atom has a positively charged central nucleus.
Observation: Some of the positive alpha particles were deflected back towards the emitter, so they were repelled by the nucleus.

4.1 Proton: (+)1 ***[1 mark]***
Neutron: 0 ***[1 mark]***

4.2 The protons and neutrons are in the central nucleus ***[1 mark]*** and the electrons surround the nucleus (arranged in shells) ***[1 mark]***.

4.3 26 electrons ***[1 mark]***. Atoms are neutral ***[1 mark]***. Protons and electrons have equal but opposite charges. For these charges to cancel, there must be the same number of each ***[1 mark]***.

Pages 228-230 — Isotopes and Nuclear Radiation

Warm-up
Gamma — weakly ionising, alpha — strongly ionising, beta — moderately ionising.

1.1 radioactive decay ***[1 mark]***

1.2 Atoms with the same number of protons ***[1 mark]*** but different numbers of neutrons (in their nucleus) ***[1 mark]***.

1.3 An atom losing (or gaining) at least one electron ***[1 mark]***.

1.4 Alpha decay ***[1 mark]***

2 E.g. Alpha particles have a small range in air and will be stopped by a thin sheet of material ***[1 mark]***. So the alpha radiation inside the detector cannot escape the detector ***[1 mark]***.

3.1 23 ***[1 mark]***

Remember that the mass number is the little number in the top-left. It's the total number of protons and neutrons in the nucleus.

3.2 23 – 11 = 12 neutrons ***[1 mark]***

The number of neutrons is the difference between the mass number and the atomic number.

3.3 $^{24}_{11}\text{Na}$ ***[1 mark]***

An isotope has the same number of protons (so the same atomic number), but a different number of neutrons (so a different mass number).

3.4 The atomic number of the neon isotope is lower, so there are fewer protons in the neon isotope ***[1 mark]***. So the charge on the neon isotope's nucleus is lower than the charge on the sodium isotope's nucleus ***[1 mark]***.

4 How to grade your answer:
Level 0: There is no relevant information. ***[No marks]***
Level 1: There is a brief explanation of the method of locating the leak and of the radiation used. ***[1 to 2 marks]***
Level 2: There is some explanation of the method of locating the leak and of the radiation used. ***[3 to 4 marks]***
Level 3: There is a clear and detailed explanation of the method of locating the leak and of the radiation used. ***[5 to 6 marks]***

Here are some points your answer may include:
The isotope travels along the pipe.
If there is no leak, the radiation doesn't escape the pipe/not much radiation can escape the pipe/some of the radiation is blocked by the pipe.
If there is a leak, the isotope escapes the pipe and some/more radiation can reach the detector.
This causes the count-rate to increase.
An increase in count-rate indicates a leak.
The isotope could be beta-emitting because beta radiation would be blocked by the pipe but would not be blocked by the small amount of ground above the pipe.
OR The isotope could be gamma-emitting because it can escape the pipe and reach the detector, and more gamma radiation would get to the detector if there was a leak.

5.1 For 0.5 mm thickness:
uncertainty = range ÷ 2 = (122 – 99) ÷ 2 = **11.5** ***[1 mark]***
For 0.6 mm thickness:
mean = (93 + 95 + 98) ÷ 3
= 95.33... = **95 (to nearest whole number)** ***[1 mark]***

5.2 The results for a thickness of 0.6 mm are the most precise, as they have the smallest range / they have the smallest uncertainty / the individual results are closest to the mean value for count-rate ***[1 mark]***. It's not possible to know whether they are the most accurate, as you can't tell from the data how close to the true value the measurements are ***[1 mark]***.

5.3 E.g. the thicker the paper, the less beta radiation reaches the detector / the more beta radiation is absorbed by the paper ***[1 mark]***.

5.4 If the half-life was shorter than or close to the duration of the experiment, the count-rate would reduce significantly during the experiment ***[1 mark]***, and it would not be possible to conclude if a decrease in count-rate was due to the paper or the decay of the substance ***[1 mark]***.

Page 231 — Nuclear Equations

1.1 It increases the positive charge on the nucleus / makes the nucleus 'more positive' ***[1 mark]***.

1.2 The atomic number increases ***[1 mark]*** but the mass number stays the same ***[1 mark]***. This is because emitting an electron (beta decay) involves a neutron turning into a proton ***[1 mark]***.

Remember that a neutron turns into a proton in order to increase the positive charge on the nucleus. (Because emitting the electron has taken away some negative charge.)

1.3 No effect ***[1 mark]***

When an electron moves to a lower energy level, it loses energy in the form of an EM wave, which doesn't change the charge or mass of the nucleus.

2.1 The atomic numbers on each side are not equal ***[1 mark]***.

2.2 ${}^{0}_{-1}e$ ***[1 mark]***

The other particle must be an electron (a beta particle), as this will balance the equation.

2.3 ${}^{226}_{88}Ra \longrightarrow {}^{222}_{86}Rn + {}^{4}_{2}He$

[3 marks in total — 1 mark for each correct symbol]

You know that the mass number of the radium is 226 (that's what 'radium-226' means). You also know that an alpha particle is ${}^{4}_{2}He$, so you can find the mass and atomic numbers of radon by balancing the equation.

2.4 Rn-222 has 222 – 86 = 136 neutrons ***[1 mark]***
2 alpha decays = 2 × 2 = 4 neutrons released ***[1 mark]***
136 – 4 = **132** ***[1 mark]***

Pages 232-233 — Half-life

1.1 E.g. the time taken for the count-rate of a sample to halve ***[1 mark]***.

1.2 75 seconds ***[1 mark]***

The initial count-rate is 60 cps. Half of this is 30 cps, which corresponds to 75 seconds on the time axis.

1.3 After 1 half-life, there will be 800 ÷ 2 = 400 undecayed nuclei remaining. After 2 half-lives, there will be 400 ÷ 2 = 200 undecayed nuclei remaining.
So 800 – 200 = **600** nuclei will have decayed.
[2 marks for correct answer, otherwise 1 mark for calculating the number of decayed/undecayed nuclei after one half-life]

1.4 After 2 half-lives, there are 200 undecayed nuclei.
The ratio is 200:800, which simplifies to **1:4** ***[1 mark]***

You don't even need the numbers to work out this ratio. For any radioactive isotope, after two half lives, the initial number of undecayed nuclei will have halved and then halved again. It will be one quarter of the original number, so the ratio is always 1:4.

2 Isotope 1, because more nuclei will decay per second ***[1 mark]***.

3.1 It takes a total of 2 hours and 30 minutes for the activity to halve from 8800 Bq to 4400 Bq,
so its half-life = (2 × 60) + 30 = **150 minutes** ***[1 mark]***

3.2 Check how many half-lives pass during 6 hours and 15 minutes:
6 hours and 15 minutes = (6 × 60) + 15 = 375 minutes
375 ÷ 150 = 2.5 half-lives
The activity can only be worked out if a whole number of half-lives have passed, so calculate how many half-lives have passed from the time when activity = 6222 Bq:
1 hour 15 minutes = 60 + 15 = 75 minutes
375 – 75 = 300 minutes, 300 ÷ 150 = 2 half-lives.
So now you can calculate the activity after 2 half-lives, with an initial activity of 6222 Bq:
After 1 half-life, the activity will be 6222 ÷ 2 = 3111 Bq
After 2 half-lives, the activity will be 3111 ÷ 2 = 1555.5 Bq
1555.5 = **1600 Bq (to 2 s.f.)**
[2 marks for correct answer, otherwise 1 mark for finding how many half-lives will have passed between 1 hour and 15 minutes and 6 hours and 15 minutes]

4.1

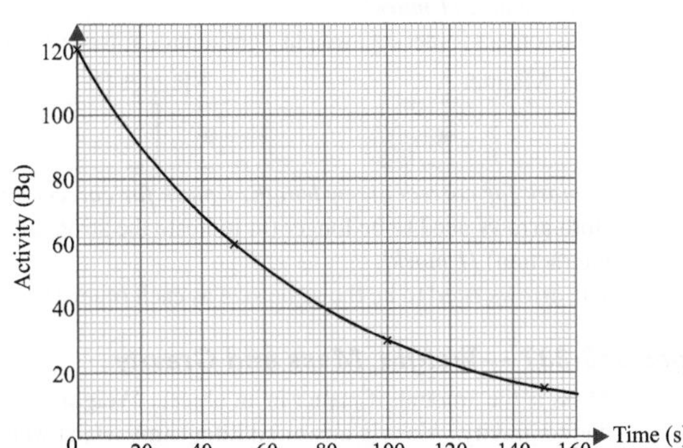

[3 marks in total — 2 marks for all points plotted correctly, otherwise 1 mark for three points plotted correctly, 1 mark for smooth curve.]

Start the graph at 120 Bq. After 50 s, this will have halved to 60 Bq. After another 50 s (i.e. 100 s altogether), it will have halved again, to 30 Bq. Plot these points, then join them up with a nice smooth curve.

4.2 70 Bq (accept between 68 Bq and 72 Bq)
[1 mark for correct value from your graph]

4.3 After 200 s, 15 ÷ 2 = 7.5 Bq
After 250 s, 7.5 ÷ 2 = **3.75 Bq** ***[1 mark]***
E.g. radioactive decay is random ***[1 mark]*** and the effect of randomness on the activity will be greater for lower activities ***[1 mark]***.

Page 234 — Irradiation and Contamination

1 Any two from: e.g. using shielding / working in a different room to the radioactive source / using remote-controlled arms to handle sources / wearing protective suits ***[2 marks]***

2.1 Contamination is when unwanted radioactive particles get onto an object ***[1 mark]***. Irradiation is when an object is exposed to radiation ***[1 mark]***.

2.2 Any two from: e.g. wearing protective gloves / using tongs / wearing a protective suit or mask ***[2 marks]***.

3 How to grade your answer:

Level 0: There is no relevant information. ***[No marks]***
Level 1: There is a brief explanation of the dangers of contamination or radiation. ***[1 to 2 marks]***
Level 2: There is some explanation of the dangers and risks of contamination and radiation. ***[3 to 4 marks]***
Level 3: There is a clear and detailed explanation of the dangers and risks of contamination and radiation, used to justify the conclusion that the clockmaker should be more concerned about

contamination. ***[5 to 6 marks]***
Here are some points your answer may include:
Alpha particles are strongly ionising.
Alpha particles are stopped by skin or thin paper.
Being irradiated won't make the clockmaker radioactive.
But irradiation may do some damage to his skin.
However, the radiation cannot penetrate his body and cause damage to his tissue or organs.
If the clockmaker's hands get contaminated with radium-226, he will be exposed to more alpha particles, close to his skin.
Or he may accidentally ingest (eat) some.
Or if particles of the radium get into the air, he could breathe them in.
The radium will then decay whilst inside his body.
This means that the alpha particles can do lots of damage to nearby tissue or organs.
So he should be more concerned about contamination.

Topic P5 — Forces

Page 235 — Contact and Non-Contact Forces

Warm-up
Scalar — mass, time, temperature
Vector — acceleration, weight, force

1 Vector quantities have both magnitude and direction. ***[1 mark]***

2 Contact force: e.g. friction / tension / normal contact force / air resistance ***[1 mark]***
Non-contact force: e.g. weight / gravitational force ***[1 mark]***

3.1
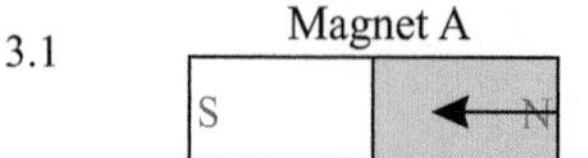

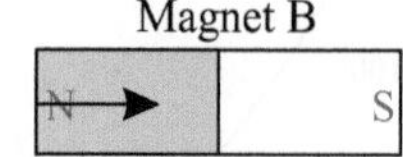

[1 mark for correct arrow length, 1 mark for correct direction]

3.2 Both arrows need to be longer (to indicate the stronger interaction) ***[1 mark]***.
The arrows need to be the same size as each other ***[1 mark]***.

Pages 236-237 — Weight, Mass and Gravity

1 **Mass** is the amount of matter in an object. **Weight** is a force due to gravity. Mass is measured **kilograms** whilst weight is measured in **newtons**. The weight of an object is **directly** proportional to its mass. ***[3 marks for all correct, 2 marks for 3-4 correct, 1 mark for 1-2 correct]***

2 A point at which you can assume the whole mass of an object is concentrated. / The point from which the weight of an object can be assumed to act. ***[1 mark]***

3.1 $W = mg$ ***[1 mark]***

3.2 $W = 350 \times 9.8$ ***[1 mark]*** = **3430 N** ***[1 mark]***

3.3 New mass = 350 – 209 = 141 kg ***[1 mark]***
$W = mg = 141 \times 3.8$ ***[1 mark]*** = 535.8
= **536 N (to 3 s.f.)** ***[1 mark]***

4.1 E.g. the standard mass may no longer have the same mass as it is labelled with ***[1 mark]***.
This is because some of the rusted standard mass is made of a different substance (the rust) instead of pure iron as when it was originally measured and labelled. Also, the rust could flake off the standard mass, leaving it with a lower mass than before.

4.2 Systematic error ***[1 mark]***, because the weight of the plastic tray will be included in each of the weight measurements, making them all too large by the same amount ***[1 mark]***.

4.3 E.g.
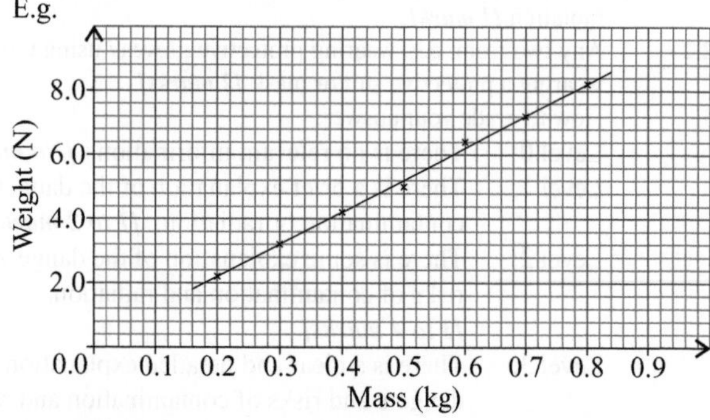

[1 mark for all points plotted correctly and 1 mark for a straight line of best fit drawn through or close to all points]

4.4 Since $W = mg$, by comparing this to the equation for a straight-line graph, $y = mx + c$, you can see that the gravitational field strength, g, is equal to the gradient of the graph, m ***[1 mark]***.
E.g. $g = \frac{\text{change in } y}{\text{change in } x} = \frac{8.4 - 2.0}{0.82 - 0.18}$ ***[1 mark]***
= **10 N/kg** ***[1 mark]***

Page 238 — Resultant Forces and Work Done

1 C ***[1 mark]***
The resultant force is the sum of the two forces acting on each runner, taking into account the direction. For runner C, the resultant force is 130 N – 100 N = 30 N.

2.1 $W = Fs = 50 \times 15$ ***[1 mark]*** = **750** ***[1 mark]***
Unit: **J** or **Nm** ***[1 mark]***

2.2 The temperature of the suitcase increases ***[1 mark]*** because doing work causes some energy to be transferred to the thermal energy store of the suitcase ***[1 mark]***.

3.1 100 N ***[1 mark]***
As the ladder isn't moving, the resultant force is zero, and so the weight of the ladder is equal to the normal contact force acting on the ladder.

3.2
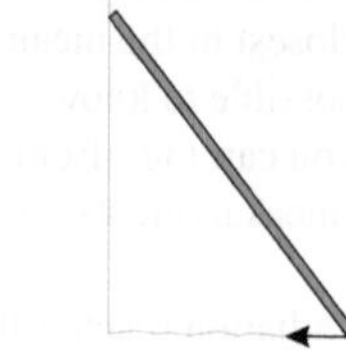
[1 mark for correct arrow length (same as 30 N arrow length), 1 mark for correct direction]

Page 239 — Calculating Forces

Warm-up
Horizontal component = 4 N, Vertical component = 3 N

1.1 1 cm = 100 N ***[1 mark]***

1.2

Magnitude = **430 N**
[1 mark for correct construction of resultant force, 1 mark for correct magnitude]

Page 240 — Forces and Elasticity

1.1 Elastic deformation is when an object returns to its original size after the deforming force is removed ***[1 mark]***. Inelastic deformation is when an object has been deformed such that it cannot return to its original size or shape after the deforming force is removed ***[1 mark]***.

1.2 Compressing, bending ***[1 mark for both correct]***

2.1 $F = ke$ so $k = F \div e$. e = 20 cm = 0.2 m
so $k = 250 \div 0.2$ ***[1 mark]*** = **1250** ***[1 mark]*** Unit = **N/m** ***[1 mark]***

2.2 E.g. Agree — the extension will be 40 cm, because force is proportional to extension, so doubling the force doubles the extension ***[1 mark]***, assuming that the spring hasn't gone past its limit of proportionality ***[1 mark]***.

Page 241 — Investigating Springs

1.1
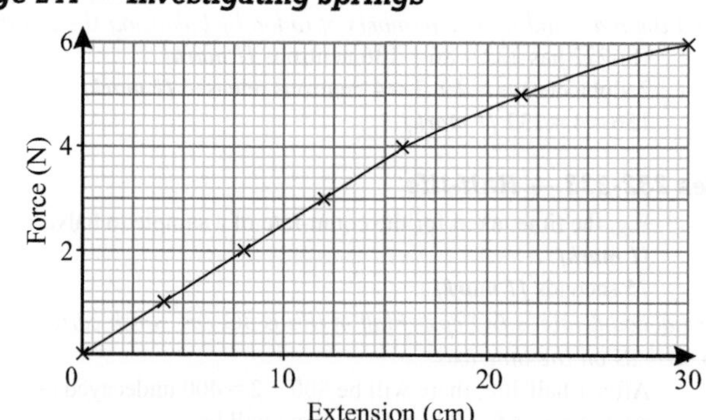

[1 mark for points plotted correctly, 1 mark for line of best fit showing linear relationship at the start, 1 mark for curved line of best fit towards the end of the graph]

1.2 Spring constant = Force ÷ Extension

= gradient of the linear section of the graph

$k = 3 \div 0.12 =$ **25 N/m**

[2 marks for correct answer between 24 and 26 N/m, otherwise 1 mark for correct calculation]

2 Work done on spring = energy stored in the spring's elastic potential energy store

$E = \frac{1}{2}ke^2 = \frac{1}{2} \times 25 \times 0.08^2$ ***[1 mark]*** = **0.08 J** ***[1 mark]***

Pages 242-243 — Distance, Displacement, Speed and Velocity

Warm-up

Displacement and **velocity** are both **vector** quantities. This means they have both a size and a direction. Speed and **distance** are both **scalar** quantities. They do not depend on direction.

1.1 7 m ***[1 mark]***

1.2 12 m ***[1 mark]***

1.3

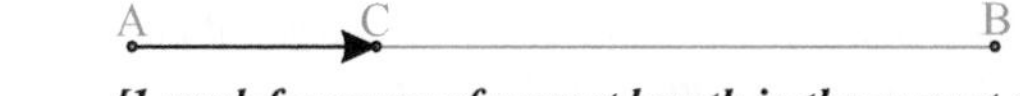

[1 mark for arrow of correct length in the correct direction]

1.4 2 m ***[1 mark]***

2 330 m/s ***[1 mark]***

3 Any three from: fitness / age / distance travelled / terrain ***[3 marks — 1 mark for each correct answer]***

4 No — velocity is speed in a given direction ***[1 mark]***. The satellite travels at a constant speed, but is always changing direction so its velocity is always changing ***[1 mark]***.

5.1 $s = vt$ ***[1 mark]***

5.2 Typical walking speed = 1.5 m/s (accept 1-2 m/s) ***[1 mark]***

$t = s \div v = 6000 \div 1.5$ ***[1 mark]***

= **4000 s** (accept 3000-6000 s) ***[1 mark]***

5.3 Typical cycling speed = 6 m/s (accept 5-7 m/s) ***[1 mark]***

$s = vt$ so $t = s \div v = 6000 \div 6$ ***[1 mark]*** = 1000 s ***[1 mark]***

4000 – 1000 = **3000 s** (accept 1800-5200) ***[1 mark]***

5.4 $t = 20 \times 60 = 1200$ s ***[1 mark]***

$s = vt$ so $v = s \div t = 9600 \div 1200$ ***[1 mark]*** = **8 m/s** ***[1 mark]***

6 Speed of sound = 331 + (0.6 × –60) = 295 m/s ***[1 mark]***

Jet speed = 0.80 × 295 = 236 m/s ***[1 mark]***

$s = vt = 236 \times 5.0 \times 10^4$ ***[1 mark]***

= 11 800 000 m = **11 800 km** ***[1 mark]***

Page 244 — Acceleration

Warm-up

A sprinter starting a race — 1.5 m/s²

A falling object — 10 m/s²

A bullet shot from a gun — 2×10^5 m/s²

1 The object is slowing down ***[1 mark]***.

2.1 $a = \Delta v \div t$ ***[1 mark]***

2.2 $a = \Delta v \div t = 4 \div 1$ ***[1 mark]*** = **4 m/s²** ***[1 mark]***

3 $t = \Delta v \div a$ ***[1 mark]*** = 20 ÷ 2.5 ***[1 mark]*** = **8 s** ***[1 mark]***

4 $v^2 - u^2 = 2as$ so

$a = (v^2 - u^2) \div 2s = (18^2 - 32^2) \div (2 \times 365)$ ***[1 mark]***

= –0.9589...

So deceleration = 1.0 m/s² (to 2 s.f.) ***[1 mark]***

Pages 245-248 — Distance-Time and Velocity-Time Graphs

1.1

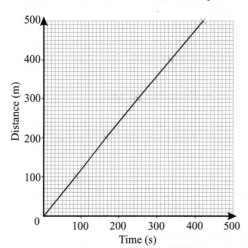

[3 marks for graph plotted correctly, otherwise 1 mark for three points correct, 1 mark for any suitable straight line]

1.2 360 m (accept between 350 m and 370 m) ***[1 mark]***

1.3 210 s (accept between 200 s and 220 s) ***[1 mark]***

1.4 E.g. refer to the same point on the boat / make sure that the timings are measured from exactly level with the posts / make sure timings are made close to the posts to avoid parallax / use a stopwatch instead of a watch ***[1 mark for any correct answer]***

2.1 12 minutes ***[1 mark]***

2.2 Accelerating ***[1 mark]***

3.1 $v = \Delta s \div t$ = gradient of line

Speed = (92 – 20) ÷ (6 – 3) = 72 ÷ 3 = **24 m/s**

(accept between 23 m/s and 25 m/s)

[3 marks for correct answer, otherwise 1 mark for realising speed is the gradient of the line, 1 mark for correct calculation]

3.2 Speed = gradient of a tangent to the line

$v = \Delta s \div \Delta t = (16 - 0) \div (3 - 1) = 16 \div 2 =$ **8 m/s**

(accept between 6 m/s and 10 m/s)

[3 marks for correct answer, otherwise 1 mark for a correct tangent to the line, 1 mark for correct calculation]

4.1

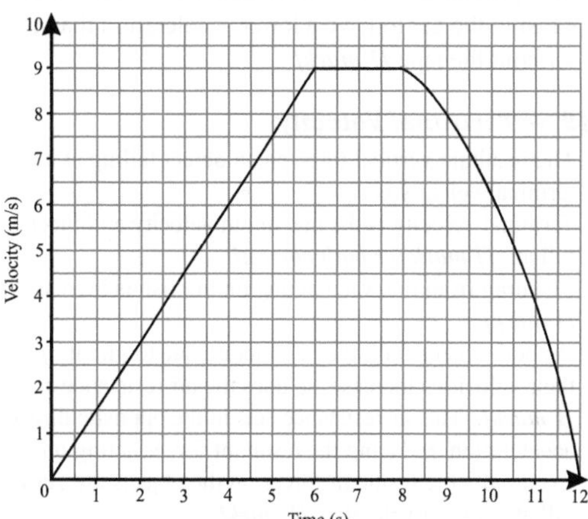

[1 mark for correct shape of graph, 1 mark for graph ending at 0 m/s]

4.2 $a = \Delta v \div t$ = gradient of the line

Acceleration = (9 – 0) ÷ (6 – 0) = **1.5 m/s²**

[2 marks for correct answer, otherwise 1 mark for correct calculation]

4.3 $s = vt$ = area under the line ***[1 mark]***

0-6 s: area = $\frac{1}{2}bh = \frac{1}{2} \times 6 \times 9 = 27$ m ***[1 mark]***

6-8 s: area = $bh = 2 \times 9 = 18$ m ***[1 mark]***

Total distance in 8 s = 27 + 18 = **45 m** ***[1 mark]***

4.4 1 square is worth 0.5 s on the x-axis (time)

1 square is worth 0.5 m/s on the y-axis (velocity)

[1 mark for both correct]

$s = vt = 0.5 \times 0.5 = 0.25$ m ***[1 mark]***

Squares under the line between 8 s and 12 s = 91 ***[1 mark]***

91 × 0.25 = 22.75 m ***[1 mark]***

Total distance = 45 + 22.75 = 67.75 = **68 m** ***[1 mark]***

(accept between 63 and 72 m)

5.1 The instantaneous acceleration can be found by finding the gradient of a tangent drawn at that point. So, draw a tangent at $t = 26$ s

E.g.

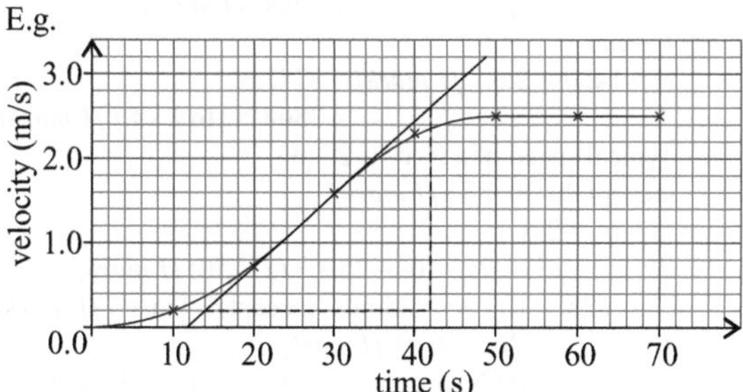

[1 mark]

$$\text{gradient} = \frac{\text{change in } y}{\text{change in } x} = \frac{2.6 - 0.2}{42 - 14}$$ ***[1 mark]***

= 0.0857...

= **0.086 m/s² (to 2 s.f.)** ***[1 mark]***

You'll get the marks here as long as you've drawn a sensible tangent at t = 26 s, and your calculation of the gradient is correct for the tangent you've drawn.

5.2 Advantage of light gates: e.g. the light gates will be able to measure both the speed of the car and the time very accurately / the light gates will be able to measure both the speed of the car and the time to a high resolution ***[1 mark]***.
Disadvantage of light gates: e.g. the measurement points have to be marked out every 50 cm, so some changes in acceleration may be missed between measurements / the car has to be kept travelling in a straight line to easily pass through the gate and provide an accurate measurement ***[1 mark]***.
Advantage of the ticker tape method: e.g. it will provide many potential data points, taken at regular time intervals / the results are less affected by deviations in the straight line path of the car ***[1 mark]***.
Disadvantage of the ticker tape method: e.g. speeds have to be calculated manually from the distance measured between marks, which may introduce errors into the values / the tape may provide a resistive force against the motion of the car, causing the car to have a lower acceleration than it would without the tape ***[1 mark]***

Page 249 — Terminal Velocity

1 The resultant vertical force on an object falling at its terminal velocity is zero.
Terminal velocity is the maximum velocity an object can fall at. ***[1 mark for both correct]***

2 The drag from the water acting on the fish is increasing. ***[1 mark]***

3.1 As both objects fall, they accelerate due to gravity ***[1 mark]***. As their velocities increase, so does the air resistance acting on them ***[1 mark]***. The air resistance acts in the opposite direction to the acceleration, reducing the resultant forces acting on each object. Eventually the resultant forces on the objects are zero and they fall at constant velocities ***[1 mark]***.

3.2 The book has a larger surface area than the ball, so experiences more air resistance ***[1 mark]***. This means that the resultant force on the book reaches zero sooner, and so it has a lower terminal velocity ***[1 mark]***.

Pages 250-251 — Newton's First and Second Laws

1 If the resultant force on a stationary object is zero, the object will remain stationary ***[1 mark]***.

2 Newton's Second Law states that the acceleration of an object is **directly** proportional to the **resultant** force acing on the object and **inversely** proportional to the **mass** of the object.
[3 marks for all correct, 2 marks for 2-3 correct, 1 mark for one correct]

3.1 E.g. friction ***[1 mark]***, air resistance / drag ***[1 mark for either]***

3.2 Resultant force on an object at a constant velocity is zero.
so 5000 = 3850 + second force
Second force = 5000 – 3850 = **1150 N**
[1 mark for correct answer]

4.1 $F = ma$ ***[1 mark]***

4.2 $F = 5.0 \times 9.8$ ***[1 mark]*** = **49 N** ***[1 mark]***

5 $a = \Delta v \div t$
$a = 24 \div 9.2$ ***[1 mark]*** = 2.6... m/s^2 ***[1 mark]***
$F = ma$
$F = 1450 \times 2.6...$ ***[1 mark]*** = 3782.6...
= **3800 N (to 2 s.f.)** ***[1 mark]***

6 Typical speed of a lorry is 25 m/s
(accept 20-30 m/s) ***[1 mark]***
$v^2 - u^2 = 2as$
$a = (v^2 - u^2) \div 2s = (0^2 - 25^2) \div (2 \times 50)$ ***[1 mark]***
$= -625 \div 100 = -6.25$ m/s^2 (accept 4-9 m/s^2) ***[1 mark]***
$F = ma = 7520 \times -6.25$ ***[1 mark]***
= **(–) 47 000 N** (accept 30 100-67 700 N) ***[1 mark]***

Page 252 — Inertia and Newton's Third Law

Warm-up

When two objects interact, they exert equal and opposite forces on each other.

1.1 320 N ***[1 mark]***

1.2 Normal contact force ***[1 mark]***

1.3 640 N ***[1 mark]***
Weight is the force exerted by the Earth on the gymnast (because of the gymnast and the Earth interacting). An equal but opposite force acts on the Earth because of the gymnast.

2.1 The tendency to continue in the same state of motion ***[1 mark]***

2.2 E.g. how difficult it is to change the velocity of an object / ratio of force over acceleration / $m = F \div a$
[1 mark for any correct definition]

Page 253 — Investigating Motion

1.1 E.g. as force increases, so does acceleration / acceleration is proportional to force
[1 mark for any correct conclusion]

1.2 $F = ma$ ***[1 mark]***

1.3 At a force of 4.0 N, the acceleration is 2.25 m/s^2
So $m = F \div a$ ***[1 mark]*** = 4.0 ÷ 2.25 ***[1 mark]***
= 1.77... = **1.8 kg** ***[1 mark]***

You'll still get the marks if you took readings from a different part of the graph, so long as you get the correct final answer.

2 To test the effect of varying the mass of the trolley, the force on the trolley has to remain constant ***[1 mark]***. Adding masses to the trolley increases both the force on and mass of the trolley, so the effect of varying the mass cannot be found ***[1 mark]***.

Page 254 — Stopping Distances

1.1 The distance travelled during the driver's reaction time ***[1 mark]***

1.2 The distance travelled under the braking force of the vehicle ***[1 mark]***

2 Stopping distance = thinking distance + braking distance
12 + 24 = **36 m** ***[1 mark]***

3 Work is done by friction between the brakes and the wheels ***[1 mark]***. This causes energy to be transferred to the thermal energy stores of the brakes, so they increase in temperature ***[1 mark]***.

4 Level 0: There is no relevant information. ***[No marks]***
Level 1: There is a brief explanation of why good brakes and tyres are important. ***[1 to 2 marks]***
Level 2: There is an explanation of why good brakes and tyres are important with some explanation as to the safety implications of poor brakes or tyres. ***[3 to 4 marks]***
Level 3: A logical and detailed explanation is given which includes at least 2 examples of explaining the importance of having the tyres and brakes in good condition, at least 2 safety implications and at least 1 effect on stopping distance. ***[5 to 6 marks]***

Here are some points your answer may include:
A good tread depth on tyres removes water.
This means there is a large amount of grip (friction) between the road and the tyres.
This decreases the braking (and so stopping) distance in wet conditions.
It also means the car will be less likely to skid in wet conditions.
Brakes that are in good condition allow a larger braking force to be applied.
This means that the braking distance of the car is shorter.
Brakes that are in good condition are also less likely to overheat under a large braking force.
So the car is less likely to go out of control or cause a crash.

Pages 255-256 — Reaction Times

1 0.2 - 0.9 s ***[1 mark]***

2 Any three from: tiredness / alcohol / drugs / distractions
[3 marks — 1 mark for each correct answer]

3.1 E.g. clicking a mouse when a computer screen changes colour ***[1 mark]***

3.2 Student A: (7.0 + 7.1 + 6.9) ÷ 3 = **7.0 cm** ***[1 mark]***
Student B: (8.4 + 8.2 + 8.3) ÷ 3 = **8.3 cm** ***[1 mark]***

3.3 Student A, because the average distance fallen by the ruler was less for Student A than Student B ***[1 mark]***.

3.4 E.g. use the same ruler, always have the same person dropping the ruler. ***[2 marks — 1 mark for each correct answer]***

3.5 Their reaction times will get longer *[1 mark]*.

4 Hold a ruler between the open forefinger and thumb of the person being tested *[1 mark]*. Align their finger to the zero line of the ruler, then drop the ruler without warning *[1 mark]* and have the test subject close their thumb and finger to catch the ruler *[1 mark]*. The distance the ruler falls can be read from the ruler *[1 mark]*. The time taken for it to fall can be calculated, as the acceleration (due to gravity) is constant. This is the reaction time of the test subject *[1 mark]*.

5 Level 0: There is no relevant information. ***[No marks]***

Level 1: There is a brief explanation of how the man's reaction time may be affected and at least one mention of an implication this has for safety. ***[1 to 2 marks]***

Level 2: There is an explanation of how the man's reaction time may be affected and the implications this has for safety. ***[3 to 4 marks]***

Here are some points your answer may include:
Listening to loud music may mean that the driver is distracted. This may increase his reaction time.
An increased reaction time means an increased thinking distance.
Driving quicker also increases the distance the car travels during the man's reaction time.
All of these things increase stopping distance, which means the man may not be able to stop in time to avoid hitting a hazard.
He may be unable to see an upcoming hazard because it is dark.
Driving late at night might mean that the man is tired.
He may not be able to hear an upcoming hazard because of the loud music.
This reduces the stopping distance required to avoid hitting a hazard and may lead to the driver having a collision.

6 $v^2 - u^2 = 2as$
$v^2 = 0 + (2 \times 9.8 \times 0.45)$ *[1 mark]* = 8.82
$v = 2.969...$ m/s *[1 mark]*
$a = \Delta v \div t$
$t = \Delta v \div a = 2.969... \div 9.8$ *[1 mark]*
$= 0.303... =$ **0.30 s (to 2 s.f.)** *[1 mark]*

Page 257 — Momentum

Warm-up

1: Momentum is a property of...
2: ...moving objects.
3: It is a...
4: ...vector quantity and is equal to...
5: ...mass × velocity.

1.1 $p = mv$ *[1 mark]*

1.2 $m = p \div v$ *[1 mark]* = 5500 ÷ 25 *[1 mark]* = **220 kg** *[1 mark]*

2 In Figure 1, the total momentum of the system is equal to the mass of the moving ball multiplied by its velocity *[1 mark]*. As it hits the line of balls, it transfers this momentum to them and comes to a stop. All of this momentum is transferred along the line of balls to the ball at the end of the line, which is why the middle balls don't move *[1 mark]*. This final ball has the same momentum as the first ball, causing it to move with the same velocity (because all of the balls have the same mass) that the moving ball in Figure 1 had *[1 mark]*. In Figure 2, the total momentum of the system is equal to the total momentum in Figure 1 *[1 mark]*.

Topic P6 — Waves

Page 258 — Transverse and Longitudinal Waves

1.1 Wave A is a **transverse** wave and wave B is a **longitudinal** wave. *[1 mark]*

1.2 E.g.

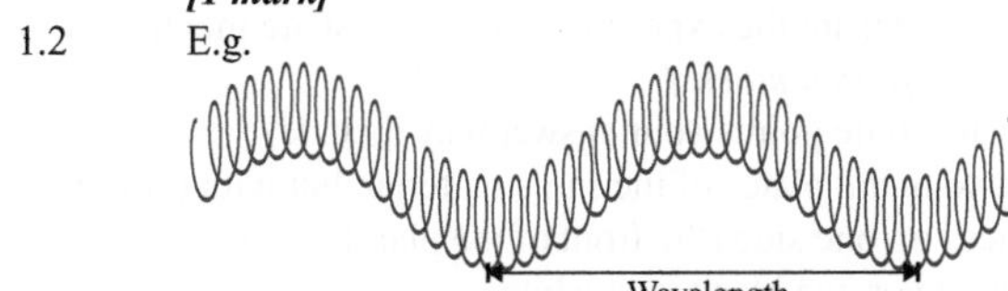

[1 mark for correctly labelled wavelength]

1.3 Amplitude is the maximum displacement of a point on a wave from its undisturbed position *[1 mark]*.

1.4 E.g. ripples on the surface of water / light / any other electromagnetic wave *[1 mark]*

2.1 Horizontal arrow drawn pointing away from the loudspeaker *[1 mark]*

2.2 $T = 1 \div f = 1 \div 200$ *[1 mark]* = **0.005 s** *[1 mark]*

2.3 In longitudinal waves, the oscillations/vibrations are parallel to the wave's direction of energy transfer *[1 mark]*, but in transverse waves, the oscillations/vibrations are perpendicular/at right angles to the wave's direction of energy transfer *[1 mark]*.

Page 259 — Experiments with Waves

1.1 E.g. the student could use a strobe light *[1 mark]*. When the frequency of the strobe light matches that of the wave, the wave fronts will appear stationary (and the student can then measure the stationary wave) *[1 mark]*.

1.2 There are 9 wavelengths in the distance of 18 cm.
Therefore, wavelength = 18 cm ÷ 9 = 2 cm *[1 mark]*
$v = f\lambda = 12 \times 0.02$ *[1 mark]*
= **0.24 m/s** *[1 mark]*

2 How to grade your answer:

Level 0: There is no relevant information. ***[No marks]***

Level 1: A simple method to find the speed of waves on a string is partly outlined. ***[1 to 2 marks]***

Level 2: A method to find the speed of waves on a string is outlined in some detail. ***[3 to 4 marks]***

Level 3: A method to find the speed of waves on a string using suitable apparatus is fully explained in detail. ***[5 to 6 marks]***

Here are some points your answer may include:
Connect a string over a pulley to a vibration transducer.
Connect a signal generator to the vibration transducer and switch it on.
Adjust the frequency of the signal generator to produce clear waves on the string.
For as many half-wavelengths on the string as you can, measure the distance they cover.
Divide this by the number of half-wavelengths to find the average half-wavelength of the waves on the string.
Double this value to find the wavelength, λ, and note down the frequency of the frequency generator, f.
Use the formula $v = f\lambda$ to calculate the speed of the waves on the string, v.
To get more accurate results the experiment can be repeated for different frequencies and a mean value calculated.

Page 260 — Wave Behaviour and Electromagnetic Waves

Warm-up

wave is reflected — it bounces back off the material
wave is absorbed — it transfers all energy to the material
wave is transmitted — it passes through the material unaffected

1.1 All waves in the electromagnetic spectrum are **transverse**. *[1 mark]*. All electromagnetic waves travel at the same speed in **a vacuum**. *[1 mark]*

1.2 microwaves *[1 mark]*

1.3 E.g. energy is transferred from the thermal energy store of a toaster's heating element *[1 mark]* by (infrared) radiation to the thermal energy store of bread inside the toaster *[1 mark]*.

2 Some of the light is reflected back *[1 mark]* and some of the light is transmitted through the lens *[1 mark]*.

Page 261 — Refraction

1.1

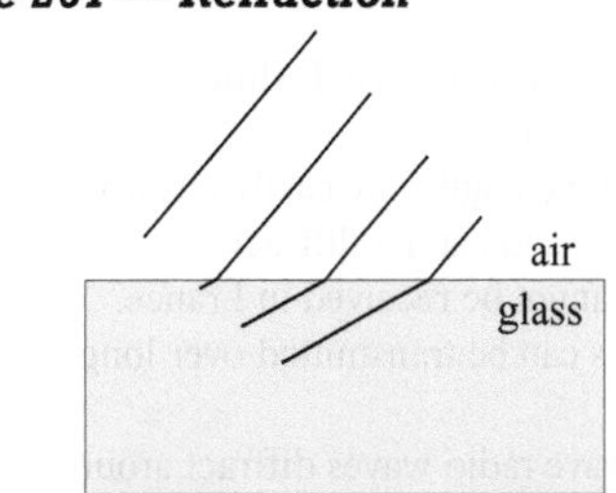

[1 mark for wave fronts bending in the correct direction, 1 mark for wave fronts inside the glass being joined up with those in the air.]

1.2

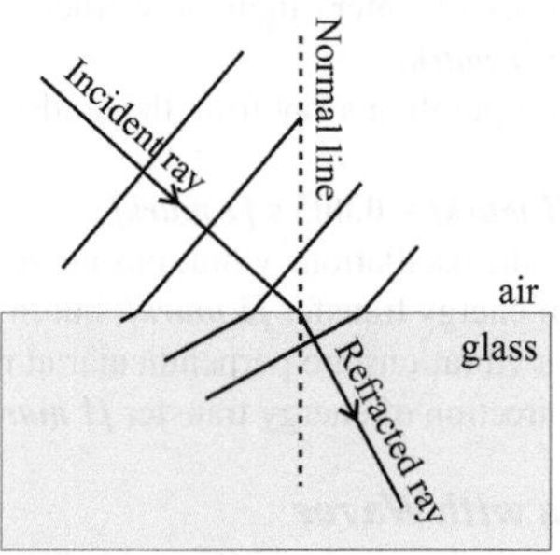

[1 mark for incident ray drawn and labelled correctly, 1 mark for normal line drawn and labelled correctly, 1 mark for refracted ray drawn and labelled correctly.]

2.1 The ray bends towards the normal as it crosses the boundary ***[1 mark]***.

2.2 The light ray would bend away from the normal ***[1 mark]*** because it would speed up / because light travels slower in glass than in a vacuum ***[1 mark]***.

Page 262 — Radio Waves

Warm-up

True, True, False, True.

1 How to grade your answer:

Level 0: There is no relevant information. ***[No marks]***

Level 1: A simple method of generating radio waves is described. ***[1 to 2 marks]***

Level 2: A method of generating radio waves and how these waves generate an electrical signal in a distant TV aerial is described. ***[3 to 4 marks]***

Here are some points your answer may include:

An alternating current flows in the circuit the transmitter is connected to.

Alternating currents are made up of oscillating charges/electrons.

As the electrons oscillate in the transmitter, they produce oscillating electric and magnetic fields/radio waves.

Radio waves are transmitted to and then absorbed by the distant TV aerial.

The energy carried by the waves is transferred to the electrons in the material of the receiver.

This causes electrons in the receiver aerial to oscillate.

This generates an alternating current/an electrical signal.

This alternating current has the same frequency as the original current used to generate the radio wave.

2 How to grade your answer:

Level 0: There is no relevant information. ***[No marks]***

Level 1: There is a brief explanation of the differences between radio wave types used for broadcasting ***[1 to 2 marks]***

Level 2: There is some explanation of the differences between radio wave types used for broadcasting, including their different ranges and how this affects which broadcast can be heard. ***[3 to 4 marks]***

Level 3: There is a clear and detailed explanation of the differences between radio wave types used for broadcasting, including their different ranges and how this affects which broadcast can be heard. ***[5 to 6 marks]***

Here are some points your answer may include:

FM radio is transmitted using very short wavelength radio waves.

These radio waves can only be received while the receiver is in direct sight of the transmitter.

This is because these wavelengths are easily absorbed by obstacles, e.g. buildings, and cannot diffract.

Therefore, the signal cannot be received in France.

Long-wave radio waves can be transmitted over long distances.

This is because long-wave radio waves diffract around the curved surface of the Earth.

Long-wave radio waves can also diffract around obstacles such as mountains.

Hence the signal can be received in France.

Page 263 — EM Waves and Their Uses

1.1 The microwaves are absorbed by water molecules in the potato ***[1 mark]***. This transfers energy to the water molecules, causing the water in the potato to heat up ***[1 mark]***. The water molecules transfer the energy they have absorbed to the rest of the molecules in the potato, cooking it ***[1 mark]***.

1.2 The glass plate does not absorb any microwaves ***[1 mark]*** as it does not contain any water molecules, and so it does not heat up ***[1 mark]***.

1.3 infrared ***[1 mark]***

1.4 Satellites are located above the atmosphere ***[1 mark]***. The atmosphere contains water molecules ***[1 mark]***. The microwaves used in microwave ovens could not reach satellites as they would be absorbed by water molecules in the atmosphere ***[1 mark]***. Different wavelengths which are not absorbed by the atmosphere must be used to communicate with satellites ***[1 mark]***.

2 It is dark so there is very little visible light for a normal camera to pick up ***[1 mark]***. The person trying to hide is warmer than the surroundings and so emits more infrared radiation ***[1 mark]***. This makes the person stand out from the surroundings if observed through infrared radiation ***[1 mark]***.

Page 264 — More Uses of EM Waves

Warm-up

UV Rays: A, C, D
Visible Light: B
X-rays: E, F
Gamma Rays: F

1.1 E.g. the patient is injected with a gamma-emitting source ***[1 mark]***. Gamma radiation is detected outside of the body, which is used to follow the source's progress around the patient's body ***[1 mark]***.

1.2 E.g. they can pass out of the patient's body / they can be detected outside of the patient's body ***[1 mark]***.

1.3 X-rays are directed at the patient. The X-rays are absorbed by bones ***[1 mark]***, but transmitted by less dense body material, such as flesh ***[1 mark]***. A screen behind the patient detects the X-rays and a negative image is formed with brighter areas where fewer X-rays are detected ***[1 mark]***.

1.4 E.g. wear lead aprons / stand behind lead screens / leave the room whilst treatment is taking place ***[1 mark]***.

Pages 265-266 — Investigating Infrared Radiation

1.1 Matte black ***[1 mark]***

1.2 Shiny white ***[1 mark]***

1.3 E.g. use a radiation detector to measure the emitted radiation / use a ruler to make sure he measures the radiation emitted from each side from the same distance ***[1 mark for any sensible suggestion]***

2 How to grade your answer:

Level 0: There is no relevant information. ***[No marks]***

Level 1: There is a brief description of the apparatus used to investigate the absorption of different surfaces. ***[1 to 2 marks]***

Level 2: There is some description of a method and apparatus to investigate the absorption of different surfaces. At least one method to ensure the experiment is a fair test is mentioned. ***[3 to 4 marks]***

Level 3: There is a clear and detailed description of a method and apparatus to investigate the absorption of different surfaces. At least two methods to ensure the experiment is a fair test are mentioned. ***[5 to 6 marks]***

Here are some points your answer may include:

Use two metal plates of the same material, but with different surfaces on one side (the front of the plate) — e.g. one shiny, one matte or one black, one white.

The plates should be the same size and thickness / identical in all other ways to make it a fair test.

On the back of each plate, a ball bearing is attached with candle wax.
The ball bearings should be identical to make the experiment a fair test.
The amount of wax used to attach each ball bearing should be the same, to ensure the test is fair.
The front of the plates are then faced towards a lit bunsen burner.
The distance between each plate and the bunsen burner should be the same to ensure the experiment is a fair test.
The time taken for the wax to melt and the ball bearing to fall is measured for both plates using a stopwatch.
The stopwatch should be stopped at the same point for each plate (e.g. the ball bearing starting to fall, or hitting the table/floor) for it to be a fair test.
The times taken for each ball bearing can then be compared to see which surface is better at absorbing radiation.
The faster the time, the better the surface is at absorbing radiation.

3.1 Any three from: e.g using the same mass of water in each can / using the same equipment for each can / starting measurements at the same temperature for each can / using cans that are the same size and shape / using cans that are made from the same material ***[3 marks]***.

Each of these make sure that the rate of change of temperature is only affected by the paint on the can, not any other properties of the cans, the water, or the experimental set-up. This ensures that it is a fair test, and so the experiment will produce valid results.

3.2 E.g. the water in can A / the can painted with matt navy blue paint will cool fastest ***[1 mark]***. This is because dark and matt surfaces are better emitters of infrared radiation than light and shiny/glossy surfaces ***[1 mark]***.

3.3 E.g.

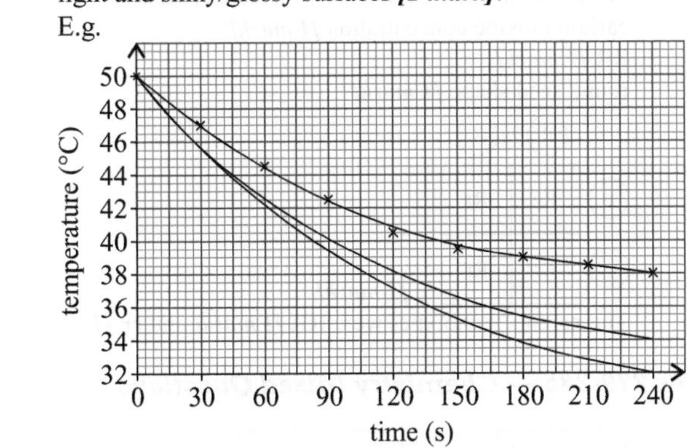

[1 mark for all points drawn correctly, and 1 mark for a smooth curve of best fit which passes through or close to all the points]

Page 267 — Dangers of Electromagnetic Waves

1.1 X-rays and gamma rays transfer so much energy to living cells that they can knock off electrons (ionise atoms) ***[1 mark]***. This can cause mutation of genes, leading to cancer ***[1 mark]***.

1.2 Any two from: sunburn / premature aging / blindness / (increased risk of) skin cancer ***[2 marks]***

2.1 Compare risk of chest scan to risk of head scan,
$10\,000 \div 2500 = 4$
Risk is 4 times greater, so dose is 4 times greater ***[1 mark]***.
Dose = 2×4 = **8 mSv** ***[1 mark]***

2.2 How to grade your answer:
Level 0: There is no relevant information. ***[No marks]***
Level 1: The risks and benefits are identified but no comparison is made about whether one outweighs the other. ***[1 to 2 marks]***
Level 2: There is some discussion about balancing the benefits with the risks. ***[3 to 4 marks]***
Level 3: There is a detailed explanation of the benefits and risks, and an informed explanation of why the procedure may go ahead. ***[5 to 6 marks]***

Here are some points your answer may include:
The radiation dose is large, so the risk of developing cancer from the procedure is higher than in some other procedures.
However, the procedure might better inform a decision on future treatment.
So future treatment may be more effective.
The benefit of treating the condition needs to be compared with the risk of the procedure (and any subsequent treatment).
An assessment needs to be made about the risk of dying (or poor quality of life) from the underlying condition and the potential benefits for treatment.
Other less risky procedures might lead to similar benefits and these need to be considered.
If the benefits outweigh the risks considerably, then it is worth carrying on with the procedure.

Topic P7 — Magnetism and Electromagnetism

Pages 268-269 — Permanent and Induced Magnets

Warm-up
non-contact

1.1 A region in which a magnet or magnetic material will experience a force ***[1 mark]***.

1.2 Any two of e.g. iron/steel/nickel/cobalt ***[2 marks]***

1.3

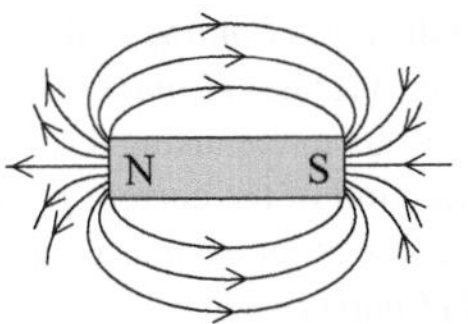

[2 marks in total — 1 mark for correct shape, 1 mark for arrows pointing from north to south]

1.4 The correct statements are:
The closer together the magnetic field lines, the stronger the magnetic field ***[1 mark]***.
Magnetic field lines point from the north pole to the south pole of a magnet ***[1 mark]***.

2.1 The block of cobalt becomes an induced magnet when it is placed in the magnetic field of the bar magnet ***[1 mark]***, which causes a force of attraction between the paperclip and the cobalt ***[1 mark]***

2.2 When the bar magnet is removed, the cobalt will quickly demagnetise ***[1 mark]***, so the paperclip will become unstuck ***[1 mark]***.

3.1 How to grade your answer:
Level 0: There is no relevant information. ***[No marks]***
Level 1: There is a brief description of how the compass should be used. ***[1 to 2 marks]***
Level 2: There is a good description of the method used to determine the magnetic field, including the effect on a compass when placed in a magnetic field. ***[3 to 4 marks]***

Here are some points your answer may include:
The needle of a compass points in the direction of the magnetic field it is in.
Put the magnet on a sheet of paper.
Move the compass along the field lines of the horseshoe magnet.
Mark the direction of the compass needle at each point.
Join up the marks to create a diagram of the magnetic field lines.

3.2 E.g. it would point (to geographic) north ***[1 mark]*** because it is aligning itself with the magnetic field of the Earth ***[1 mark]***.

Page 270 — Electromagnetism

1.1

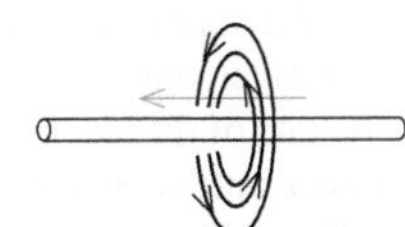

[2 marks in total — 1 mark for correct shape, 1 mark for correct direction]

You can work this out using the right-hand thumb rule — point your right thumb in the direction of the current and your curled fingers will show the direction of the field lines. Bingo.

1.2 The direction of the field will also be reversed ***[1 mark]***.

1.3 Increase the current ***[1 mark]***.

2.1 E.g. put a block of iron in the middle of the solenoid ***[1 mark]***.

2.2 Repelled ***[1 mark]***, because the direction of the current means that the left-hand end of the solenoid acts as a north pole ***[1 mark]***, and like poles repel ***[1 mark]***.

Page 271 — The Motor Effect

1 $F = BIl$, so $B = F \div Il$

$B = 1.2 \div (0.4 \times 0.75)$ ***[1 mark]*** $= 1.2 \div 0.3 =$ **4 T**

[1 mark for correct value, 1 mark for correct unit]

2 A ***[1 mark]***

The force acting on the wire is at a maximum when the wire is perpendicular to the magnetic field between the magnets (0°) and is zero when the wire is parallel to the magnetic field (90°).

Page 272 — Electric Motors

1 It will move towards you, out of the paper ***[1 mark]***.

Use Fleming's left-hand rule here. Point your first finger in the direction of the field (i.e. from the north pole to the south pole of the magnets). Point your second finger in the direction of the current (shown in the diagram). Your thumb will then show the direction of motion of the wire.

2.1 clockwise ***[1 mark]***

2.2 E.g. the interacting magnetic fields (of the coil and the magnets) causes a force on each arm of the coil ***[1 mark]*** in the opposite direction (which causes the coil to rotate) ***[1 mark]***.

2.3 E.g. swap the contacts every half turn (e.g. using a split-ring commutator) to reverse the direction of the current ***[1 mark]***. This swaps the direction of the forces for each arm and keeps the direction of rotation constant ***[1 mark]***.

Mixed Questions

Pages 273-278 — Biology Mixed Questions

1.1 E.g. producing bile / converting lactic acid to glucose / storing glucose as glycogen / breaking down amino acids ***[1 mark]***

1.2 Enzymes speed up chemical reactions in living organisms. ***[1 mark]***

1.3 pH 9 ***[1 mark]***

1.4 The enzyme will not work ***[1 mark]*** because the acid will change the shape of its active site/denature the enzyme ***[1 mark]*** and the substrate will no longer fit ***[1 mark]***.

1.5 Alcohol is a risk factor for lung cancer. ***[1 mark]***

2.1 To stop the loss of water by evaporation ***[1 mark]***.

2.2

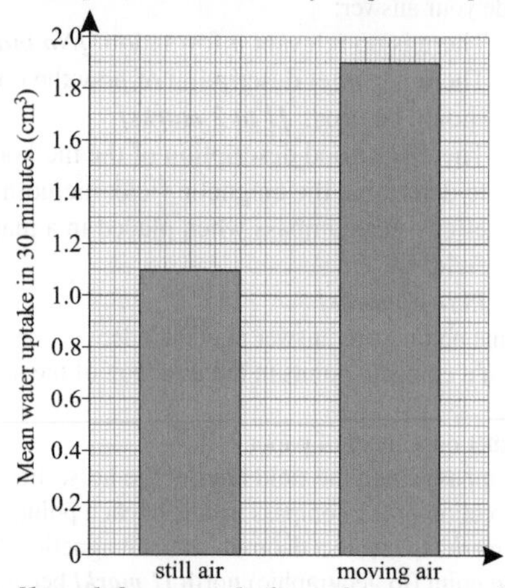

[1 mark for correctly drawn bars, one mark for correctly labelled axes.]

2.3 The greater the air flow around the plant, the greater the transpiration rate ***[1 mark]***.

2.4 E.g. increasing air flow carries more water vapour away from the plant / reduces the concentration of water vapour outside the leaves ***[1 mark]***. This increases the rate of diffusion of water from the leaf cells from an area of higher water concentration to an area of lower water concentration ***[1 mark]***.

2.5 $1.2 - 0.8 =$ **0.4 cm³** ***[1 mark]***

The range is the difference between the highest and lowest values.

2.6 30 minutes ÷ 60 = 0.5 hours

$1.9 \div 0.5 =$ **3.8 cm³/hour** ***[2 marks for correct answer, otherwise 1 mark for correct working.]***

3.1 mitochondria ***[1 mark]***

3.2 glucose + oxygen → carbon dioxide + water ***[1 mark for both reactants correct, 1 mark for both products correct.]***

3.3 Glucose is combined with nitrate ions ***[1 mark]*** to make amino acids ***[1 mark]***, which are then joined together to make proteins ***[1 mark]***.

4.1 The hormone is secreted directly into the blood ***[1 mark]***. It is then carried in the blood to the target organ ***[1 mark]***.

4.2 C ***[1 mark]***

4.3 B ***[1 mark]***

4.4 It stimulates ovulation / the release of an egg from an ovary ***[1 mark]***.

4.5 ovaries ***[1 mark]***

4.6 A constantly high level of oestrogen inhibits the production of FSH ***[1 mark]***, so there are no mature eggs for fertilisation to take place ***[1 mark]***.

5.1 oxygen ***[1 mark]***

5.2 light intensity ***[1 mark]***

5.3 Tube 1 ***[1 mark]***

5.4 Tube 1 shows that in the dark, the algae are producing more carbon dioxide than they take in ***[1 mark]***. The concentration of carbon dioxide is high because the cells are respiring, but not photosynthesising (as there's no light for photosynthesis to take place) ***[1 mark]***. Tube 2 shows that in the light, the algae are taking up more carbon dioxide than they produce ***[1 mark]***. The concentration of carbon dioxide has reduced because the cells are photosynthesising faster than they are respiring ***[1 mark]***.

5.5 Any two from: e.g. the temperature of the boiling tubes / the volume of hydrogencarbonate indicator / the concentration of hydrogencarbonate indicator / the number of beads in each tube / the concentration of algal cells in each bead ***[2 marks]***.

5.6 Light intensity ***[1 mark]*** because the rate of photosynthesis is increasing as the light intensity increases ***[1 mark]***.

5.7 carbon dioxide concentration ***[1 mark]***

6.1 RR ***[1 mark]***

6.2 round seed shape ***[1 mark]***

6.3

	R	R
r	Rr	Rr
r	Rr	Rr

[1 mark]

The parents' genotypes were **RR** ***[1 mark]*** and **rr** ***[1 mark]***.

Pages 279-285 — Chemistry Mixed Questions

1.1

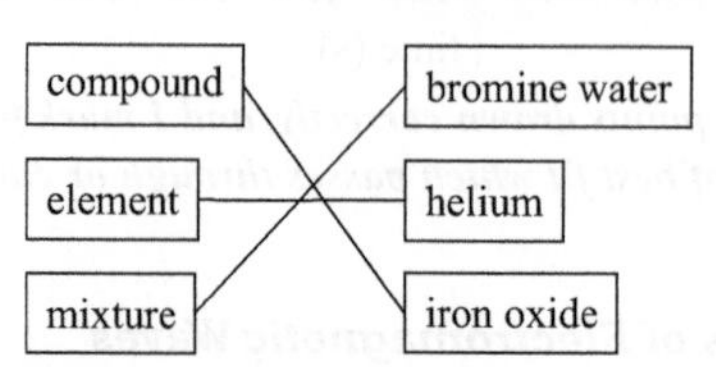

[2 marks if all three correct, otherwise 1 mark if 1 correct]

1.2 Mixtures with a precise purpose ***[1 mark]*** that are made by following a formula / a recipe ***[1 mark]***.

2.1 Dissolve the rock salt in water and filter ***[1 mark]***.

2.2 It contains two elements/more than one element in fixed proportions ***[1 mark]*** held together by chemical bonds ***[1 mark]***.

2.3 ionic ***[1 mark]***

3.1 Group: 6 ***[1 mark]***

Explanation: There are 6 electrons in the outer shell ***[1 mark]***.

3.2 2– ions ***[1 mark]***, as oxygen atoms need to gain two electrons to get a full outer shell ***[1 mark]***.

3.3 Oxidation ***[1 mark]***

4.1

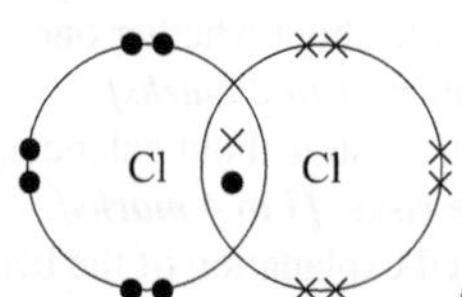

[1 mark for shared pair of electrons, 1 mark for six further electrons in the outer shell of each chlorine atom]

4.2 E.g. atoms with the same number of protons / of the same element / with the same atomic number ***[1 mark]*** with different numbers of neutrons / different mass numbers *[1 mark]*.

4.3 Hold a piece of damp litmus paper in the unknown gas *[1 mark]*. It will be bleached white in the presence of chlorine *[1 mark]*.

4.4 Chlorine is more reactive than iodine *[1 mark]*, so would displace iodine from sodium iodide solution / the solution would go from colourless to brown *[1 mark]*.

5.1 endothermic *[1 mark]*

5.2 higher *[1 mark]*

5.3 It takes more energy to break the bonds in the reactants than is released when the bonds in the products form *[1 mark]*, so overall energy is taken in from the surroundings *[1 mark]*.

5.4 E.g. in a sports injury pack *[1 mark]*.

6.1 alkanes *[1 mark]*

6.2 (fractional) distillation *[1 mark]*

6.3 cracking *[1 mark]*

6.4 Decane *[1 mark]*, because the molecules are bigger *[1 mark]*, so will have stronger intermolecular forces / more energy is needed to break the forces between the molecules *[1 mark]*.

6.5 $C_5H_{12} + 8O_2 \rightarrow 5CO_2 + 6H_2O$ ***[1 mark for correct reactants and products, 1 mark for balancing]***

7.1 The electrons in the outer shell *[1 mark]* of the metal atoms are delocalised *[1 mark]*. There is strong electrostatic attraction between the positive metal ions and the shared negative electrons *[1 mark]*.

7.2 Iron: solid *[1 mark]*. Silver: liquid *[1 mark]*

7.3 Iron *[1 mark]*, because it has a higher melting/boiling point *[1 mark]*, so more energy is needed to break the bonds *[1 mark]*.

8.1 Copper is lower in the reactivity series/less reactive than carbon *[1 mark]*, so can be extracted by reduction using carbon *[1 mark]*.

8.2 Bacteria are used to convert copper compounds in the ore into soluble copper compounds *[1 mark]*. This produces a leachate that contains copper ions *[1 mark]* which can be extracted by electrolysis/displacement with iron *[1 mark]*.

8.3 The atoms in copper form layers which slide over each other, so it can be drawn out into wires *[1 mark]*. Copper contains delocalised electrons which are free to move and carry an electric charge *[1 mark]*.

8.4 The tin atoms in bronze distort the structure of the copper *[1 mark]*. This means the layers can no longer slide over each other *[1 mark]*, so bronze is harder than copper *[1 mark]*.

9.1 It described atoms as having a tiny, positively charged nucleus at the centre *[1 mark]*, surrounded by a cloud of electrons *[1 mark]*.

9.2 Atoms consist of a small nucleus *[1 mark]* which contains the protons and neutrons *[1 mark]*. The electrons orbit the nucleus in fixed energy levels/shells *[1 mark]*.

10.1 The particles in a gas expand to fill any container they're in *[1 mark]*. So the particles of carbon dioxide formed will expand out of the unsealed reaction vessel *[1 mark]*, causing the mass of substance inside the reaction vessel to decrease *[1 mark]*.

10.2 E.g. add a set volume and concentration of hydrochloric acid to the reaction vessel *[1 mark]*. Add a set volume and concentration of sodium carbonate solution *[1 mark]*, connect the reaction flask to a gas syringe *[1 mark]* and start the stop-watch *[1 mark]*. Record the volume of gas collected at regular intervals until the reaction is finished *[1 mark]*. Repeat the experiment, keeping everything the same except for the concentration of acid *[1 mark]*.

10.3 Change in volume = 12.0 cm^3

Mean rate of reaction = $\frac{\text{amount of product formed}}{\text{time}}$

$= \frac{12.0}{30}$ = **0.40 cm^3/s** ***[2 marks for correct answer, otherwise 1 mark for using the correct equation to calculate rate]***

11.1 Any two from: e.g. it dissolved in oceans / photosynthesis / trapped in rocks and fossil fuels ***[2 marks — 1 mark for each correct answer]***

11.2 E.g. methane *[1 mark]*. It is increasing due to more agriculture / waste production *[1 mark]*.

11.3 How to grade your answer:

Level 0: There is no relevant information. ***[No marks]***

Level 1: There are a few examples of other pollutant gases, but little discussion of how they are made or what their impacts could be. ***[1 to 2 marks]***

Level 2: There are a number of examples of other pollutant gases, with some discussion of how they are made and what their impacts could be. ***[3 to 4 marks]***

Level 3: There are a number of examples of other pollutant gases, with a detailed discussion of how they are made and what their impacts could be. ***[5 to 6 marks]***

Here are some points your answer may include:
Other pollutant gases include carbon monoxide, sulfur dioxide and nitrogen oxides.
Carbon monoxide is produced when fuels undergo incomplete combustion.
Carbon monoxide can cause fainting, coma or even death.
Sulfur dioxide is produced when fuels that contain sulfur impurities are burned.
Sulfur dioxide can mix with water in clouds to produce sulfuric acid, so cause acid rain.
Sulfur dioxide can cause respiratory problems.
Nitrogen oxides are produced when nitrogen and oxygen from the air react/combine due to the heat of burning.
Nitrogen oxides can mix with water in clouds to produce nitric acid, so cause acid rain.
Nitrogen oxides can cause respiratory problems.

12.1 $M_r(\text{LiOH}) = A_r(\text{Li}) + A_r(\text{O}) + A_r(\text{H}) = 7 + 16 + 1 =$ **24** ***[1 mark]***

12.2 Number of moles = mass ÷ molar mass = 1.75 ÷ 7 = **0.25 mol** ***[2 marks for correct answer, otherwise 1 mark for using the correct equation to calculate moles]***

12.3 From the reaction equation, 0.50 mol Li forms 0.50 mol LiOH. Mass of LiOH = number of moles × molar mass = 0.50 × 24 = **12 g** ***[3 marks for correct answer, otherwise 1 mark for number of moles of LiOH produced, 1 mark for using the correct equation to calculate mass]***

13.1 Zinc is more reactive than hydrogen *[1 mark]*. This means zinc forms positive ions more easily than hydrogen *[1 mark]*.

13.2 Reduction *[1 mark]*, because the hydrogen ions gain electrons *[1 mark]*.

13.3 $4OH^- \rightarrow O_2 + 2H_2O + 4e^-$ ***[1 mark for correct reactants and products, 1 mark for balancing]***

If you had '$-4e^-$' on the left hand side of the equation instead of '$+4e^-$' on the right, you still get the marks.

14.1 How to grade your answer:

Level 0: There is no relevant information. ***[No marks]***

Level 1: There is a brief description of the similarities and differences between lithium and sodium, but no explanation of these observations. ***[1 to 2 marks]***

Level 2: There is a detailed comparison of the similarities and differences between lithium and sodium, and some explanation of the observations. ***[3 to 4 marks]***

Level 3: There is a detailed comparison of the similarities and differences between lithium and sodium, and a good explanation of the observations. ***[5 to 6 marks]***

Here are some points your answer may include:
Both react to form positive, 1+ ions.
Both elements are in Group 1, so have one electron in their outer shell.
Not much energy is needed to remove this one outer electron and give the elements a full outer shell of electrons.
Both react with acid.
Sodium reacts more vigorously with acid than lithium.
Sodium is lower down in the group, so the outer electron in sodium is further away from the nucleus than the outer electron in lithium.
The attraction between the outer electron and the nucleus of sodium is less than the attraction between the outer electron and the nucleus in lithium.
Less energy is needed to remove the outer electron of sodium, making it more reactive than lithium.

14.2 Any answer in the range 80–160 °C *[1 mark]*

Pages 286-292 — Physics Mixed Questions

1.1 E.g. a permanent magnet produces its own magnetic field *[1 mark]*. An induced magnet is a material that on becomes magnetic when it is put in a magnetic field *[1 mark]*.

1.2

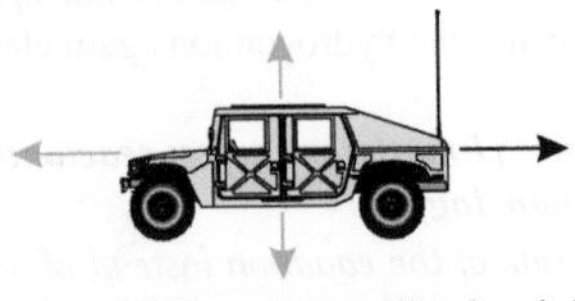

[1 mark for field lines pointing in the correct direction, 1 mark for drawing straight, parallel field lines inside the coil, 1 mark for drawing the field outside the coil]

2.1 Radioactive decay is where a nucleus releases radiation to become more **stable**. It is a **random** process, which means you **cannot** predict which individual nucleus in a sample will decay next. *[2 marks for all correct, otherwise 1 mark for two correct]*

2.2 E.g. The rate of decay of a source of unstable nuclei/a radioactive source *[1 mark]*.
It is measured in becquerels/Bq *[1 mark]*.

2.3 E.g. the time taken for the activity of a sample to halve *[1 mark]*.

3.1 three-core cable *[1 mark]*

3.2 Live — **brown** — **230** *[1 mark]*
Neutral — blue — **0** *[1 mark]*
Earth — **green and yellow** — 0 *[1 mark]*

3.3 Energy is transferred **electrically** from the mains supply to the **kinetic** energy store of the fan's blades. *[1 mark for each correct answer]*

3.4 Energy transferred = Power × Time = 30 × (30 × 60) *[1 mark]*
= **54 000 J** *[1 mark]*

4.1 C *[1 mark]*

4.2 $V = IR$ *[1 mark]*

4.3 $R = V \div I = 240 \div 1.2$ *[1 mark]* = **200 Ω** *[1 mark]*

5.1 water ripples, gamma rays *[1 mark for both correct]*

5.2 $T = 1 \div f = 1 \div 40$ *[1 mark]* = 0.025 s
0.025 × 1000 *[1 mark]* = **25 ms** *[1 mark]*

5.3 $v = f\lambda$ *[1 mark]*

5.4 $v = 40 \times 0.6$ *[1 mark]* = **24 m/s** *[1 mark]*

6.1

[1 mark for an arrow in the right direction, 1 mark for it being the same length as the driving force arrow]

6.2 $s = vt$ *[1 mark]*

6.3 $s = 5.0 \times 30$ *[1 mark]* = **150 m** *[1 mark]*

6.4 $E_k = \frac{1}{2}mv^2$
$E_k = \frac{1}{2} \times 0.50 \times 5.0^2$ *[1 mark]* = **6.25 J** *[1 mark]*

6.5 Efficiency = Useful output energy transfer ÷ Total input energy transfer *[1 mark]*

6.6 0.65 = Useful output energy transfer ÷ 1200
Useful output energy transfer = 0.65 × 1200 *[1 mark]*
= **780 J** *[1 mark]*

7.1 increasing acceleration *[1 mark]*
steady speed *[1 mark]*
constant acceleration *[1 mark]*

7.2 Acceleration = gradient of the graph *[1 mark]*
Acceleration = $\Delta v \div \Delta t = (7 - 4) \div (7 - 5)$ *[1 mark]*
= 3 ÷ 2 = **1.5 m/s²** *[1 mark]*

7.3 $F = ma$. So $a = F \div m$ *[1 mark]* = (–)440 ÷ 83 *[1 mark]*
= (–)5.30... m/s²
So deceleration = **5.3 m/s²** *[1 mark]*

Remember, force is a vector quantity. It's negative here because it's acting in the opposite direction to the motion of the cyclist. That's what gives you a negative acceleration (deceleration).

7.4 Distance travelled whilst reacting (thinking distance):
Assume a 0.5 s reaction time (accept 0.2-0.9 s) *[1 mark]*
From the graph, the cyclist's speed is 7 m/s, so:
$s = vt = 7 \times 0.5 = 3.5$ m (accept 1.4-6.3 m) *[1 mark]*
Distance travelled whilst braking (braking distance):
$v^2 - u^2 = 2as$, $u = 7$ m/s, $v = 0$, $a = -5.3$ m/s
$s = (v^2 - u^2) \div 2a = (0^2 - 7^2) \div (2 \times -5.3)$ *[1 mark]*
$= -49 \div -10.6 = 4.62...$ m *[1 mark]*
Stopping distance = thinking distance + braking distance
= 3.5 + 4.62... = 8.12... m = 8.1 m
(accept 6.0-11.0 m)
Stopping distance is less than 12 m, so the cyclist won't hit the car *[1 mark]*.

8.1 E.g.

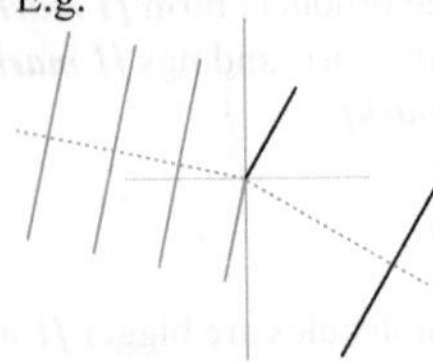

[1 mark for wave fronts correctly changing direction, 1 mark for wave fronts being spaced further apart]

8.2 How to grade your answer:
Level 0: There is no relevant information. *[No marks]*
Level 1: There is a brief description of how the speed of different parts of the wave front change between air and diamond. *[1 to 2 marks]*
Level 2: There is a good description of how different parts of a wave front travel at different speeds when crossing a boundary. There is some description of how this results in refraction. *[3 to 4 marks]*
Level 3: There is a detailed explanation of how the difference in speed for different parts of a wave front results in a difference in distance travelled. There is a clear description of how this results in refraction when crossing a boundary at an angle. *[5 to 6 marks]*

Here are some points your answer may include:
Light travels faster in air than it does in diamond.
When the light ray crosses the boundary between diamond and air at an angle, it means different parts of the wave front cross the boundary at different times.
The parts of the wave front that have crossed the boundary travel faster than the rest of the wave front that is still travelling through the diamond.
Distance = speed ÷ time. So in the time it takes the entire wave front to cross over the boundary, the parts of the wave front that have spent more of that time travelling through air have travelled further. This difference in distance travelled between points along the wave front causes the ray to bend (refract) away from the normal.

9.1 E.g.

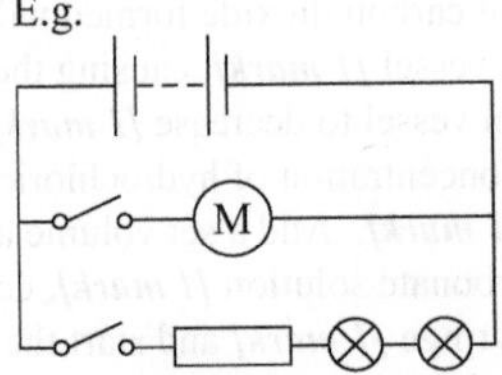

[2 marks for all circuit symbols correctly drawn, otherwise 1 mark for 4 symbols correctly drawn. 1 mark for filament lamps and resistor in series with each other, 1 mark for motor in parallel with other components, 1 mark for correct placement of switches]

9.2 $E = QV$ and $Q = It$ so $E = VIt$ *[1 mark]*
$E = 6.0 \times 70.0 \times 10^{-3} \times (15 \times 60)$ *[1 mark]* = 378 J
$\Delta E = mc\Delta\theta = 0.0250 \times 120 \times 6$ *[1 mark]* = 18 J
378 – 18 *[1 mark]* = **360 J** *[1 mark]*

9.3 E.g. he could lubricate the parts within the motor *[1 mark]*. This would reduce friction and the amount of energy being wasted/dissipated to the thermal energy store of the motor *[1 mark]*.

ISBN 978 1 78294 490 4
9 781782 944904
SAHQA42

CGP — books like no others!

www.cgpbooks.co.uk